Target 

Get back on track

German

Reading

Lisa Probert

Published by Pearson Education Limited, 80 Strand, London, WC2R 0RL.

www.pearsonschoolsandfecolleges.co.uk

Produced by Out of House Publishing
Typeset by Newgen KnowledgeWorks Pvt. Ltd., Chennai, India

First published 2017

20 19 18
10 9 8 7 6 5 4 3 2

British Library Cataloguing in Publication Data
A catalogue record for this book is available from the British Library

ISBN 978 0435 18910 5

Printed in Great Britain by Ashford Colour Press Ltd.

Note from the publisher
Pearson has robust editorial processes, including answer and fact checks, to ensure the accuracy of the content in this publication, and every effort is made to ensure this publication is free of errors. We are, however, only human, and occasionally errors do occur. Pearson is not liable for any misunderstandings that arise as a result of errors in this publication, but it is our priority to ensure that the content is accurate. If you spot an error, please do contact us at resourcescorrections@pearson.com so we can make sure it is corrected.

This workbook has been developed using the Pearson Progression Map and Scale for German.

To find out more about the Progression Scale for German and to see how it relates to indicative GCSE 9–1 grades go to www.pearsonschools.co.uk/ProgressionServices

Helping you to formulate grade predictions, apply interventions and track progress.

Any reference to indicative grades in the Pearson Target Workbooks and Pearson Progression Services is not to be used as an accurate indicator of how a student will be awarded a grade for their GCSE exams.

You have told us that mapping the Steps from the Pearson Progression Maps to indicative grades will make it simpler for you to accumulate the evidence to formulate your own grade predictions, apply any interventions and track student progress. We're really excited about this work and its potential for helping teachers and students. It is, however, important to understand that this mapping is for guidance only to support teachers' own predictions of progress and is not an accurate predictor of grades.

Our Pearson Progression Scale is criterion referenced. If a student can perform a task or demonstrate a skill, we say they are working at a certain Step according to the criteria. Teachers can mark assessments and issue results with reference to these criteria which do not depend on the wider cohort in any given year. For GCSE exams however, all Awarding Organisations set the grade boundaries with reference to the strength of the cohort in any given year. For more information about how this works please visit: https://www.gov.uk/government/news/setting-standards-for-new-gcses-in-2017

Contents

1 Recognising and understanding core vocabulary

This unit will help you to recognise and understand core vocabulary. The skills you will build are to:

- recognise and understand common words
- show you have understood common words
- take account of the context of common words.

In the exam, you will be asked to tackle reading exercises like the one on these two pages. This unit will help you learn skills to respond to this type of exam question. In the exam, you will see rubrics in German and rubrics in English. In this particular question type, the rubrics are in English.

Do not answer this question yet. You will be asked to come back to it at the end of the unit.

Exam-style question

School

The school year is just about to start. Three German teenagers have written short blogs about their schools.

Read their blogs and complete the sentences in **English**.

> Natürlich ist das Gymnasium sehr schwierig, weil es viel Notendruck gibt. Ich habe Angst vor schlechten Noten, denn meine Eltern sind ziemlich streng. Wenn ich nicht erfolgreich bin, werde ich nicht nur ein schlechtes Zeugnis bekommen, sondern auch sitzen bleiben müssen. **Florian**

1 Florian finds school difficult because there is so much

....

(1 mark)

2 He is worried about getting

....

(1 mark)

3 If he is not successful, he will have to

....

(1 mark)

Man sagt, dass die neunte Klasse sehr schwierig ist. Hoffentlich nicht! Ich freue mich nicht auf die Prüfungen, denn sie sind immer total stressig. Dieses Jahr freue ich mich besonders auf die Klassenfahrt, da wir nach Berlin fahren. Berlin ist eine sehr interessante historische Stadt. Mein Lieblingsfach ist Geschichte, weil ich es einfach finde. **Tina**

4 Tina has heard that the 9th grade is very

....

(1 mark)

5 She is particularly looking forward to

....

(1 mark)

6 Tina's favourite subject is history because she finds it

....

(1 mark)

Ich habe viele Sachen für das neue Schuljahr gekauft, zum Beispiel neue Trainingsschuhe, weil meine alten Trainingsschuhe kaputt waren. Ich bin sehr sportlich und mache normalerweise oft Sport in den AGs, aber letztes Jahr habe ich mir das Bein gebrochen und ich habe nicht oft gespielt. Ich freue mich nicht darauf, dass ich um sechs Uhr aufstehen muss. Ich will nicht so früh aufwachen! **Dario**

7 Dario has bought

....

(1 mark)

8 Dario couldn't play much sport last year because

....

(1 mark)

9 Dario is not looking forward to

....

(1 mark)

The three key questions in the **skills boosts** will help you recognise, understand and respond to core vocabulary.

How do I recognise and understand common words?

How do I show I have understood common words?

How do I take account of the context of common words?

How do I recognise and understand common words?

It is important to identify the types of words you see in a reading text (for example, verbs, adjectives, nouns), as this can help you to recognise the meaning. It is also important to identify vocabulary that is linked to the question theme. Here the theme is school, so recognising key school-related vocabulary from the core vocabulary list for GCSE will help you understand the meaning of the text as a whole.

1. A student has highlighted some words in the first text of the exam-style question in different colours. Which colour represents which type of word? Complete the table below.

Adjective = word describing a noun, e.g. 'big', 'small', 'yellow'
Connective = word linking two sentences together, e.g. 'and', 'but'
Intensifier = adverb that strengthens or weakens the force of an adjective, e.g. 'very', 'quite'
Noun = a person, place or object, e.g. 'school'
Verb = word conveying an action, e.g. 'receive'

Natürlich ist das Gymnasium sehr schwierig, weil es viel Notendruck gibt. Ich habe Angst vor schlechten Noten, denn meine Eltern sind ziemlich streng. Wenn ich nicht erfolgreich bin, werde ich nicht nur sitzen bleiben müssen, sondern auch ein schlechtes Zeugnis bekommen.

Type of word	Colour	Examples from the text
Adjectives	*green*	*schwierig,*
Connectives		
Intensifiers		
Nouns		
Verbs		

2. Now use different colours to highlight different types of words in the text below and add some of them to the table, along with the English translations.

Ich freue mich auf die Schule, weil ich dieses Jahr sehr interessante neue Fächer lerne. Es ist auch total prima, dass ich meine Freunde jeden Tag sehe. Das macht viel Spaß. Ich habe Angst vor den Klassenarbeiten, weil ich sie sehr stressig finde, aber meine Lehrerinnen und Lehrer sind meistens sehr nett und geduldig.

Type of word	Examples from the text	English translations
Adjectives		
Connectives		
Intensifiers		
Nouns		
Verbs		

In the exam, it is important to be able to identify words you know and to understand how different words work together in a sentence. Highlighting and circling different types of words are techniques you can use on your exam paper.

How do I show I have understood common words?

Once you have recognised familiar key words, you need to link them to the appropriate English statements or questions in the exam task. You also need to identify key words in the English statements for which you have learned the German.

1. Using the strategies from page 4, highlight 10 key words in this text from page 3 and write the English translations above the words.

> *difficult*
> Man sagt, dass die neunte Klasse sehr schwierig ist. Hoffentlich nicht! Ich freue mich nicht auf die Prüfungen, denn sie sind immer total stressig. Dieses Jahr freue ich mich besonders auf die Klassenfahrt, da wir nach Berlin fahren. Berlin ist eine sehr interessante historische Stadt. Mein Lieblingsfach ist Geschichte, weil ich es einfach finde.

2. In the text above, find the German translations for the following and write them down. This will help you to match the correct part of the text with the appropriate statement.

   a. the 9th grade ....

   b. I am not looking forward to ....

   c. I am looking forward to ....

   d. favourite subject ....

   e. history ....

3. i Read the text below and circle key vocabulary you think might be useful to complete the three statements in English below.

   ii Using the categories in the tables on page 4, decide what types of word you have selected and annotate the words with the English meanings.

   iii Then use the correct words to complete each statement in English.

> Ich freue mich dieses Jahr auf die AGs. Am Montag spiele ich mit meiner Mannschaft Basketball. Das ist sehr lustig, weil meine Freunde mitspielen. Am Mittwoch gehe ich in meine Theatergruppe und ich freue mich auf unsere nächste Vorstellung*. Am Freitag tanze ich, denn ich finde es immer sehr entspannend. Am Wochenende mache ich meine Hausaufgaben, weil wir dieses Jahr viele Klassenarbeiten schreiben. Das ist sehr anstrengend!

* die Vorstellung = performance

   a. Tina enjoys basketball because ....

   b. She is looking forward to the theatre group's ....

   c. On Fridays she dances because ....

3 How do I take account of the context of common words?

When seeking to understand common words, use grammatical clues and context to help you. This is essential if you want to avoid mistaking the meaning of common words in different contexts.

1. Read the sentences below, which are all connected to the topic of school in some way. Write the correct English meaning of the highlighted words. Use the context to help you. Circle the words that helped you work out the meaning.

   a. In der Informatikstunde, machen wir **Computerspiele**. ....
   b. Es gibt **viele** Pflichtfächer. ....
   c. Wir haben **vier** **Stunden** pro Tag. ....
   d. Ich habe schlechte Noten und muss **sitzen bleiben**. ....
   e. In der Schule gibt es 80 Lehrer und 700 **Kinder**. ....
   f. Die Klassenzimmer sind sehr **schmutzig**. ....
   g. Ich lerne gern Mathe, denn ich kann alles **verstehen**. ....
   h. Im Gymnasium gibt es 350 **Schüler**. ....

2. Read the final blog, from page 3, again.

> Ich habe viele Sachen für das neue Schuljahr gekauft, zum Beispiel neue Trainingsschuhe, weil meine alten Trainingsschuhe kaputt waren. Ich bin sehr sportlich und mache normalerweise oft Sport in den AGs, aber letztes Jahr habe ich mir das Bein gebrochen und ich habe nicht oft gespielt. Ich freue mich nicht darauf, dass ich um sechs Uhr aufstehen muss. Ich will nicht so früh aufwachen!

   a. What grammatical clues are there? (tenses, different persons of verbs, adjectives, nouns)

   neu = new, ...

   ....

   ....

   b. What lexical clues are there? (time phrases, key vocabulary I know)

   normalerweise = normally, ...

   ....

   ....

   c. Which words are unfamiliar? How can I use the context to help me understand the meaning?

   ....

   ....

   ....

   ....

Understanding the gist of a text is the first stage. It is always helpful to read and analyse the text before looking at the exam questions.

Your turn!

Now answer the following exam-style question which requires you to practise the skills you have worked on, in particular how to recognise and understand core vocabulary. Remember to read the text through first before you attempt the questions, and use the checklist on page 8 to help you.

Remember: highlight/circle key words in the text, annotate them in English and then link them to the statements.

Exam-style question

School

The school year is just about to start. Three German teenagers have written short blogs about their schools. Read their blogs and complete the sentences in **English**.

Ich besuche eine Hauptschule. Meine Schule ist ziemlich groß und modern. Ich finde die Lehrerinnen und Lehrer sehr nett, aber manchmal auch ein bisschen streng. In der neunten Klasse gibt es viele Hausaufgaben und Klassenarbeiten, die sehr stressig sind. Dieses Jahr freue ich mich auf die Projektwochen, denn wir werden etwas Praktisches* lernen. **Sascha**

* *praktisch* = practical

1 Sascha's school is quite

....

(1 mark)

2 He finds his teachers

....

(1 mark)

3 He is looking forward to the project weeks because

....

(1 mark)

Ich gehe auf eine private internationale Schule. Ich gehe gern in die Schule, weil meine Freundinnen und Freunde aus verschiedenen Ländern und Kulturen kommen. In der neunten Klasse gibt es viele Pflichtfächer. Man kann auch Französisch oder Spanisch und Musik oder Kunst wählen. Nach der Schule kann man viele Aktivitäten machen. Letztes Jahr habe ich Arabisch gelernt. **Anja**

Make sure you know the meaning of the highlighted words. How can you use the context to work out the meaning?

4 Anja's school friends come from

....

(1 mark)

5 Apart from the compulsory subjects, you can also learn

....

(1 mark)

6 Last year Anja

....

(1 mark)

Your turn!

> Meine Schule ist ein sehr altes Gymnasium. Das Hauptgebäude* ist sehr schön und man hat es letztes Jahr renoviert. Ich bin in der Mittelstufe. Dieses Jahr freue ich mich auf das neue Fach PGW (Politik–Gesellschaft–Wirtschaft), denn es wird sehr interessant sein. Ich lerne auch Englisch, Spanisch und Französisch, weil ich Fremdsprachen** sehr gern lerne. **Finn**

* *das Hauptgebäude* = main building

** *Fremdsprachen* = foreign languages

7 The main building in Finn's school

....

(1 mark)

8 This year Finn is looking forward to

....

(1 mark)

9 He is learning three languages because

....

(1 mark)

Checklist **Before I give my answers, have I …**	✓
recognised the meaning of common words?	
understood the meaning of common words?	
used circling/highlighting if necessary to help me understand?	
worked out what types of word I have circled/highlighted?	
linked the words in the text to the exam questions?	

Review your skills

Check up

Review your response to the exam-style question on pages 7–8. Tick the column to show how well you think you have done each of the following.

	Not quite	Nearly there	Got it!
recognised and understood common words	☐	☐	☐
shown I have understood common words	☐	☐	☐
taken account of the context of common words	☐	☐	☐

Need more practice?

Go back to pages 2–3 and do the exam-style question there.

Top tips to help you to learn the core vocabulary:

1. Look, cover, write, check.

   Write out the words you want to learn in German and in English, then cover the German and write the German translation next to each English word. Then check which words you know and look back over the ones you don't know. Keep coming back to your lists to review them and see how many more words you know each time.

2. Testing times

   Test yourself in timed conditions. Set a timer and see how many words you can correctly translate into or out of German in one minute. Keep a note of the ones you get wrong to revisit later. You could use your own flashcards or create some using online flashcard sites or apps.

How confident do you feel about each of these **skills**? Colour in the bars.

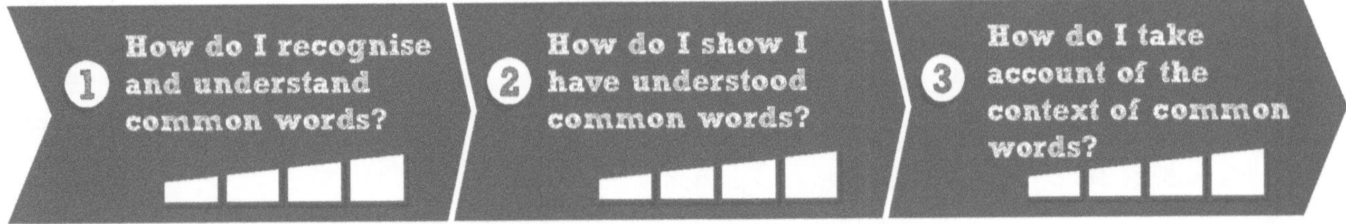

1 How do I recognise and understand common words?
2 How do I show I have understood common words?
3 How do I take account of the context of common words?

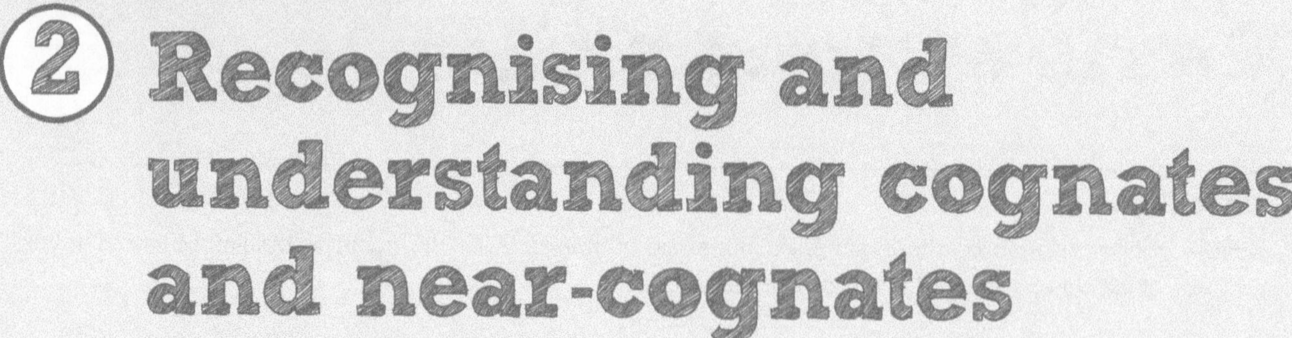

2 Recognising and understanding cognates and near-cognates

This unit will help you to recognise and understand cognates and near-cognates. The skills you will build are to:

- identify cognates
- identify near-cognates
- identify 'false friends'.

In the exam, you will be asked to tackle reading exercises like the two on these pages. This unit will help you develop the skills to respond to these types of exam questions.

Do not answer this question yet. You will be asked to come back to it at the end of the unit.

Exam-style question

Mein Lieblingshobby

Lies den Text über die Freizeitaktivitäten von Markus.

> Schwimmen ist mein Lieblingshobby und ich schwimme fast jeden Morgen, bevor ich zur Schule gehe. Danach frühstücke ich Joghurt mit Bananen, weil ich viel Energie brauche. Ich gehe immer zu Fuß zur Schule, weil ich Athlet bin und fit bleiben will.
>
> Obwohl ich lieber im Freibad als im Hallenbad schwimme, schwimme ich am liebsten im See. Ich wohne in Bayern und hier gibt es viele Badeseen, die im Sommer sehr schön sind.
>
> Nach der Schule mache ich oft Wassersport, weil das aufregend ist. Ich fahre gern Kajak und gehe gern segeln, weil ich im Boot sehr glücklich bin. Ich werde bald windsurfen lernen. Das sieht toll aus!

Schreib **R**, wenn die Aussage **richtig** ist,
F, wenn die Aussage **falsch** ist,
NT, wenn die Aussage **nicht im Text** ist.

1 Markus geht jeden Tag schwimmen. **(1 mark)**

2 Er geht nach dem Schwimmen zur Schule. **(1 mark)**

3 Um fit zu bleiben, rennt Markus zur Schule. **(1 mark)**

4 Er schwimmt lieber draußen. **(1 mark)**

5 Markus wohnt neben einem See. **(1 mark)**

6 Seiner Meinung nach ist Wassersport spannend. **(1 mark)**

7 Er fühlt sich im Boot gut. **(1 mark)**

8 Markus ist schon einmal windsurfen gegangen. **(1 mark)**

Get started

Do not answer this question yet. You will be asked to come back to it at the end of the unit.

Exam-style question

Cinema

Read the contributions by four teenage girls on a web forum page, where young people exchange information about their favourite films.

Write the first letter of the correct name in the box.

Write **J** for **Jana**.

Write **B** for **Bettina**.

Write **K** for **Karolina**.

Write **S** for **Sophia**.

Ich gehe sehr oft ins Kino, weil ich ein großer Kinofan bin. Ich sehe am liebsten Liebesfilme und Komödien, weil ich sie amüsant finde. Abenteuerfilme sehe ich nicht gern, denn ich finde sie doof. Vor kurzem habe ich ‚Honig im Kopf' gesehen. Es ging um ein Mädchen und ihren Großvater. Dieser Film war hervorragend. **Jana**

Komödien finde ich ab und zu lustig, aber oft blöd. Ich sehe lieber ausländische Filme, besonders auf der großen Leinwand. Letzten Monat bin ich mit meiner Freundin ins Kino gegangen und wir haben einen japanischen Zeichentrickfilm gesehen. Er war sehr kreativ und hat mir sehr gut gefallen. **Bettina**

Ich sehe jeden Samstag einen neuen Film, weil meine Familie sich für Filme interessiert. Wir haben einen neuen Flachbildschirm und sehen gern zusammen Filme. Wir sehen alles außer Horrorfilmen. Meine Lieblingsfilme sind historische Filme, weil sie wunderschön sind. **Karolina**

Ich gehe nicht oft ins Kino, weil das so teuer ist. Ich sehe lieber amerikanische Serien auf meinem Tablet. Am liebsten sehe ich Krimis und Dramen und manchmal sehe ich auch Fantasyserien. Letztes Wochenende habe ich meinen Geburtstag zu Hause mit meinen Freundinnen gefeiert. Wir haben Filme gesehen und Pizza gegessen. **Sophia**

1 Who has been to the cinema recently? ☐ **(1 mark)**

2 Who doesn't really watch many films? ☐ **(1 mark)**

3 Who really enjoyed a film about a family? ☐ **(1 mark)**

4 Who prefers watching films with her family? ☐ **(1 mark)**

5 Who goes to the cinema most frequently? ☐ **(1 mark)**

6 Who watched films to celebrate a birthday? ☐ **(1 mark)**

The three key questions in the skills boosts will help you recognise and understand cognates and near-cognates.

 **How do I identify cognates?**

 **How do I identify near-cognates?**

 **How do I identify 'false friends'?**

How do I identify cognates?

Words that share a common origin or that are borrowed from different languages are often the same in both English and German (cognates, e.g. *Party*) or very similar (near-cognates, e.g. *Familie*). They can help you to understand texts.

① Read the text below and put the correct cognate from the box into each gap.

Tennis	Rafting	Horrorfilme	Reggae	Thrillers	Tablet

In meiner Freizeit treibe ich gern Sport. Mein Lieblingssport ist .... Ich mache auch gern Wassersportarten wie .... Zu Hause lese ich gern auf meinem .... Meine Lieblingsbücher sind .... Ich gehe gern ins Kino und meistens sehe ich .... Ich bin auch Musikfan und höre besonders gern ....

② Look back at the exam-style questions on pages 10 and 11. Find the cognates listed below in the exam-style question texts and complete the table, underlining the differences.

Similarities and differences to look out for include:
- same spelling
- similar spelling
- an extra letter or letters
- a missing letter or letters
- capital letter in English and/or in German
- gender of German nouns: masculine, feminine or neuter?

English word	German word	What are the similarities/ differences?	Gender of German cognate
athlet<u>e</u>	*Athlet*	*Same but without 'e' at the end*	*Masculine*
drama			
fan			
fantasy			
film			
find			
fit			
hobby			
horror			
pizza			
sport			
tablet			

How do I identify near-cognates?

In addition to the cognates you listed on the previous page, there are also many words which differ slightly in their written form but have the same meaning in German and English. This is also due to their common origin or because they are words which have been borrowed. Identifying these words can really increase your understanding of vocabulary and help you to understand the detail in texts.

1. Look back through the texts in the exam-style questions on pages 10 and 11.

   a. Can you find at least one near-cognate for each letter of the alphabet listed below? Write it on the line.

   b. What do these near-cognates mean in English? Write the translation next to each German word.

A *amüsant = amusing, amerikanische =* ....

B ....

E ....

F ....

H ....

I ....

J ....

K ....

L ....

O ....

S ....

W ....

Look at the list of near-cognates. There are patterns which will help you to work out the meanings of other near-cognates. For example, adjectives ending '–ing' in English will sometimes become adjectives ending *-ant* in German and many adjectives which end *-isch* in German have the English endings '-al', '-an', '-ese' or '-ish'.

2. Thinking about the patterns you have observed in the texts and the tip above, write out the spellings in German of the words listed below.

   a. interesting = ...
   b. English = ...
   c. Chinese = ...
   d. Spanish = ...
   e. musical = ...
   f. allergic = ...
   g. fantastic = ...
   h. amusing = ...

3 How do I identify 'false friends'?

Some words which look like cognates or near-cognates are in fact 'false friends'. Although these words have the same or a similar form to the English word, they actually have a very different meaning. If you are not sure whether a word is a cognate, near-cognate or 'false friend', it can be helpful to translate the whole sentence into English to test out whether the translated word makes sense in the context.

1. In the sentences in the second column of the table below, underline the 'false friend'. Then complete the table.

	German sentence	'False friend'	English word it looks like	What it means in this context	How you worked it out
a	Am Gymnasium lerne ich Deutsch und Mathe.	*Gymnasium*	*gym(nasium)*	*grammar school*	*from the context – you study there*
b	Der See ist in der Mitte von Deutschland.				
c	Das ist mein neues Handy.				
d	Ich will einen neuen Computer kaufen.				
e	Ich werde bald windsurfen gehen.				
f	Wir sind fast da.				
g	Ich segle gern im Boot.				
h	Der Chef ist sehr nett.				

2. Underline the correct option to complete the sentences below. One is a 'false friend'. Write the meaning of each word to explain your choice. You may use a dictionary.

a Zu Weihnachten gebe ich gern Gift / Geschenke. *Gift = poison, Geschenke = presents*

b Ich sehe gern Komödien, weil sie lustig / komisch sind. ....

c In der Zukunft bekomme / werde ich Fußballspieler. ....

d Extremsportarten sind sehr gefährlich. Bist du sehr mutig / brav?

....

e Trägst du gern einen Rock / Boote? ....

f Ich esse sehr gern Pickel / Gurken. ....

Your turn!

Here is an exam-style question which requires you to practise the skills you have worked on, in particular how to recognise the meanings of cognates, near-cognates and 'false friends'.

Remember that you might find cognates, near-cognates and 'false friends' in the rubric and the questions as well as in the text.

Exam-style question

Freizeit

Lies den Text über Musik.

Musik ist mein Leben! Ich höre jeden Tag Musik – in meinem Zimmer, im Schulbus, nach der Schule und vor der Schule. Zu Weihnachten habe ich ein Tablet bekommen und ich habe jetzt eine große Musiksammlung. Am liebsten höre ich Popmusik und R&B, aber ich höre auch gern klassische Musik, besonders Opernmusik.

Ich spiele drei Instrumente und möchte noch andere Instrumente lernen. Ich spiele seit zehn Jahren Klavier, seit drei Jahren Klarinette und im Moment lerne ich Gitarre spielen. Im Gymnasium spiele ich im Orchester und ich singe auch im Chor. Meine Freunde sind alle sehr musikalisch und am Wochenende spielen wir im Stadtorchester.

In den Sommerferien werden wir ein Konzert in der Stadtmitte geben. Ich freue mich schon darauf. Letztes Jahr sind wir nach England gefahren und haben dort gespielt. Das hat viel Spaß gemacht! **Tanja**

Schreib **R**, wenn die Aussage **richtig** ist,
F, wenn die Aussage **falsch** ist,
NT, wenn die Aussage **nicht im Text** ist.

1 Tanja hört sehr oft Musik. **(1 mark)**

2 Zu Hause hört sie am liebsten House-Musik. **(1 mark)**

3 Tanja lernt in der Schule Musik. **(1 mark)**

4 Tanja will neue Instrumente spielen. **(1 mark)**

5 Tanja singt auch sehr gern. **(1 mark)**

6 Tanja spielt mit Freunden Musik. **(1 mark)**

7 Im Sommer wird sie nach England fahren. **(1 mark)**

8 Letztes Jahr hat sie ein Konzert im Ausland gegeben. **(1 mark)**

? *R&B* is a cognate. What other cognates can you find in the text?

? Make sure you know the meaning of the highlighted word, which is a near-cognate. How can you work out the meaning?

? *Gymnasium* is a 'false friend'. What other 'false friends' are there in the text?

Your turn!

Here is a second exam-style question for you to work through. It requires you to practise the skills you have worked on, in particular how to recognise the meaning of cognates, near-cognates and 'false friends'.

Exam-style question

Festivals

Read the contributions by four teenage girls on a web forum page, where young people exchange information about their favourite festivals.

Write the first letter of the correct name in the box.

Write **J** for **Janina**.

Write **B** for **Barbara**.

Write **K** for **Katja**.

Write **S** for **Sabine**.

Bald ist Karneval! Meiner Meinung nach ist Karneval das beste Festival, weil es so lebhaft ist. In unserer Stadt gibt es Festzüge, Musik, Tanz, Partys und sehr bunte Kostüme. Man isst viele Süßigkeiten wie zum Beispiel Berliner oder Fastnachtskuchen. Das Rezept von meiner Großmutter ist sehr lecker! **Janina**

Bei uns ist das größte Volksfest der Zwiebelmarkt. Er findet im Oktober statt und es gibt fast 600 Stände (Bier, Zwiebeln, Imbiss und Wein) aus Deutschland, Polen, Frankreich, Finnland und Ungarn. Man kann tolle Spezialitäten essen – Zwiebelkuchen, Zwiebelzopf, Zwiebelfleisch, Mutzbraten oder Bratwurst. **Barbara**

In meiner Stadt feiern wir jedes Jahr ein Jodlerfest. Es dauert drei Tage und es kommen 15 000 Jodler, Fahnenschwinger und Alphornbläser. Ich singe und jodle, also ist das für mich ein sehr großes Event. Mein Vater ist der offizielle Fotograf und hat während des Wochenendes viel zu tun. **Katja**

Ich wohne mit meinen Eltern in einer Pension in der Stadtmitte von Aachen. Im Dezember kommen viele Gäste, um den Weihnachtsmarkt zu besuchen. Für Kinder gibt es ein Karussell und einen speziellen Krippenweg. Man kann Lebkuchen, kandierte Äpfel, geröstete Mandeln, Waffeln und Würste essen und Kinderpunsch trinken. **Sabine**

1 Whose parents own a hotel? ☐ **(1 mark)**

2 Who has a favourite family recipe? ☐ **(1 mark)**

3 Whose parent has an important role in a festival? ☐ **(1 mark)**

4 Whose favourite festival is international? ☐ **(1 mark)**

5 Whose festival has special activities for children? ☐ **(1 mark)**

6 Whose festival is a musical festival? ☐ **(1 mark)**

Review your skills

Check up

Review your response to the exam-style questions on pages 15 and 16. Tick the column to show how well you think you have done each of the following.

	Not quite	Nearly there	Got it!
identified cognates			
identified near-cognates			
identified 'false friends'			

Need more practice?

Go back to pages 10 and 11 and do the exam-style questions there. Use the checklist below to help you.

Checklist Before I give my answers, have I ...	
identified cognates?	
understood the meaning of near-cognates?	
identified 'false friends'?	
worked out the meaning of the 'false friends'?	

Top tips to help you recognise 'false friends' in the exam:

1. Identifying cognates, near-cognates and 'false friends' is an extremely useful skill to develop when working with unfamiliar vocabulary in texts.
2. Make a list of 10–15 'false friends' you have seen before.
3. Spend time learning the 'false friends' as this will help you in your preparation for the exam.

How confident do you feel about each of these **skills**? Colour in the bars.

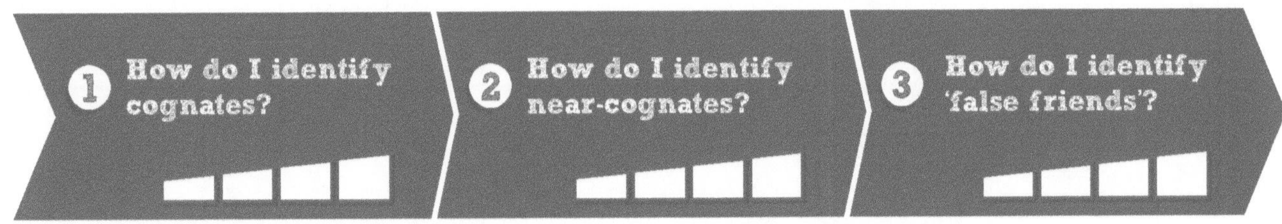
1 How do I identify cognates?
2 How do I identify near-cognates?
3 How do I identify 'false friends'?

3 Recognising and understanding grammatical clues

This unit will help you to recognise and understand grammatical clues. The skills you will build are to:

- understand how words relate to each other in a sentence
- understand different verb tenses
- understand pronouns.

In the exam, you will be asked to tackle reading exercises like the two on these pages. This unit will prepare you to respond to these types of exam questions.

Do not answer this question yet. You will be asked to come back to it at the end of the unit.

Exam-style question

Family and free time

Read the conversation in a Swiss chat room between three teenagers about activities with their families.

Write the **four** correct free-time activities in the table.

Ich verstehe mich sehr gut mit meinen Eltern, weil sie mich unterstützen. Ich bin sehr sportlich und spiele oft mit meinem Vater Tennis. Als ich jünger war, ging ich oft mit meiner Mutter schwimmen, aber heute spiele ich lieber Tennis. In den Ferien werden wir in die Alpen fahren, weil wir Ski laufen wollen. Ich freue mich darauf! **Axel**

Als ich ein Kind war, durfte ich viel machen. Meine Eltern waren nicht streng und ich durfte am Wochenende mit ihnen ins Kino gehen. Heute verbringe ich in der Woche viel Zeit mit meinen Freunden, aber am Wochenende gehe ich oft mit meinen Eltern ins Restaurant. In den Ferien werde ich mit meinem Bruder nach England fahren. Wir werden einen Englischkurs machen. **Toni**

Als ich klein war, spielte ich mit meiner Schwester Hockey. Wir gingen jeden Samstag zum Hockeyclub. Jetzt darf ich keinen Sport treiben, weil ich zu viele Hausaufgaben habe. Ich verstehe mich sehr gut mit meiner Schwester und wir spielen ab und zu Tischtennis im Garten. Nächstes Jahr werde ich in einem Club Federball spielen. Mein Vater spielt gern Federball und es freut mich, mit meinem Vater Zeit zu verbringen. **Benno**

	Past	Present	Future
Axel	*swimming*	*tennis*	*skiing*
Toni			*English course*
Benno	*hockey*		

(4 marks)

Get started

Do not answer this question yet. You will be asked to come back to it at the end of the unit.

Exam-style question

My family

Your German exchange partner writes to discuss what she is and isn't allowed to do at home. Read the e-mail and answer the questions in **English**.

Von: angela@mail.de
Betreff: Familie und Freizeit
Ich verstehe mich ziemlich gut mit meinen Eltern. Meine Mutter hat immer Zeit für mich und ich kann mit ihr über alles reden. Sie ist aber ziemlich streng und gibt mir kein Taschengeld. Als ich ein Kind war, durfte ich am Wochenende in den Park gehen. Heute darf ich das nicht machen, weil ich am Wochenende arbeite. Ich darf nicht oft mein Handy benutzen, weil das sehr teuer ist. Mein Vater unterstützt mich, aber er sagt, dass ich nicht genug Hausaufgaben mache. Ich habe schlechte Noten und darf nach der Schule keine Aktivitäten machen, weil ich meine Schularbeit machen muss. Im Moment darf ich den Computer auch nicht benutzen, weil ich so viele Schularbeit habe. Ab und zu darf ich auf Partys gehen, aber ich darf nicht alleine ausgehen. Meine Eltern sagen, ich darf nicht vor dem Fernseher sitzen. Meine Schwester darf jeden Tag drei Stunden fernsehen, also finde ich das unfair!

What is Angela **not** allowed to do? List **six** things.

1 ....

2 ....

3 ....

4 ....

5 ....

6 ....

(6 marks)

The three key questions in the **skills boosts** will help you recognise and understand grammatical clues, especially different verb tenses.

How do I understand how words relate to each other in a sentence?

How do I understand different verb tenses?

How do I understand pronouns?

Skills boost

How do I understand how words relate to each other in a sentence?

In order to understand how words relate to each other in a sentence, you have to be aware of the grammar of the sentence, for example, is there a verb with a subject and an object?

1 Read the sentences below, then answer the questions. The subject, verb and direct object have been highlighted in different colours.

Ich spiele Tennis.	Ich habe schlechte Noten.
Ich mache Leichtathletik.	Ich darf den Computer benutzen.
Ich finde Federball spannend.	Sie ist ziemlich streng.
Heute arbeite ich.	Sie darf fernsehen.

Remember that the subject does the action of the verb, and the direct object directly experiences the verb. The verb is the 'doing word' which describes the action. In German, direct objects are in the **accusative** case.

a Which colour represents the subject? ....

b Which colour represents the verb? ....

c Which colour represents the direct object? ....

d How would you annotate the words that aren't highlighted: time phrase, adjective or qualifier?

e What is the usual order of the subject, verb and direct object?

....

f What happens to the word order when you start a sentence with a time phrase?

....

g What happens to the word order when you use a modal verb (*darf*)?

....

2 Read the sentences below. Highlight the subject, verb and direct object (if there is one) in each sentence using different colours.

a Ich spiele Basketball.

b Sie sieht fern.

c Wir essen Pizza.

d Im Moment trinken wir Orangensaft.

e Wir dürfen ausgehen.

f Ich spiele gern Golf, weil das spannend ist.

3 Circle Ⓐ the indirect objects and underline A the direct objects in the sentences below as in the example.

a Sie gibt (mir) <u>kein Taschengeld</u>.

b Ich kann ihr nichts sagen.

c Ich zeige meinen Freunden unser neues Haus.

d Ich will dir eine Geschichte erzählen.

Remember that indirect objects are the noun or pronoun at which the direct object is aimed. They often follow a preposition. For example: I give the book **to her**.
In German, indirect objects are in the **dative** case.

2 How do I understand different verb tenses?

It is extremely important to learn verb forms, especially the common patterns and the differences between past, present and future tenses.

Knowing verb endings is essential in helping to understand verbs in a sentence. The verb endings tell you who the verb refers to – I, you, he/she/it, we, you or they.

1 For each of the sentences below, underline the verbs and write down the tense used.

a Als ich klein war, spielte ich mit meiner Schwester Hockey.
Imperfect tense ....

b Wir gingen jeden Samstag zum Hockeyclub.
....

c Jetzt darf ich keinen Sport treiben, weil ich zu viele Hausaufgaben habe. ....

d Nächstes Jahr werde ich in einem Club Federball spielen. ....

e Mein Vater spielt gern Federball und es freut mich, mit meinem Vater Zeit zu verbringen.
....

The **future** tense always uses *werden* as an auxiliary.

The **perfect** tense always uses *haben* or *sein* as an auxiliary.

The **present** tense only has one part to it unless it is a separable verb.

2 Using the verb table, complete the sentences below by translating the verbs into English.

Infinitive	Present tense	Imperfect tense	Future tense
dürfen *to be allowed to*	ich darf du darfst er/sie/es darf	ich durfte	ich werde … dürfen
können *to be able to, can*	ich kann du kannst er/sie/es kann	ich konnte	ich werde … können
müssen *to have to, must*	ich muss du musst er/sie/es muss	ich musste	ich werde … müssen

a Als ich jünger war, musste ich jeden Morgen schwimmen.
When I ....*was*.... younger, I ....*had*.... to swim every morning.

b Ich muss viel trainieren.
I .... to train a lot.

c Als ich ein Kind war, durfte ich viel machen.
When I .... a child, I .... to do a lot.

d Als ich klein war, durfte ich Hockey spielen.
When I .... little, I .... to play hockey.

e Ich konnte zwei- oder dreimal pro Woche spielen.
I .... play two or three times per week.

Remember to use time phrases and other context clues to help you to work out which tense is being used. For example: *als* = when (in the past), *wenn* = if, *heute* = today.

3 How do I understand pronouns?

In order to understand how words relate to each other in a sentence, you need to be able to pick out and understand the different pronouns used.

1 Look at the pronoun table below. In the sentences which follow, use different colours to highlight the subject, direct object and indirect object pronouns.

Subject	ich	du	er	sie	es	wir	ihr	Sie	sie
Direct object	mich	dich	ihn	sie	es	uns	euch	Sie	sie
Indirect object	mir	dir	ihm	ihr	ihm	uns	euch	Ihnen	ihnen

a Ich gehe mit ihnen aus.

b Sie hat immer Zeit für uns.

c Sie gibt es mir.

d Ich darf ihn benutzen, wenn er fertig ist.

e Ich finde sie sehr teuer.

f Wir geben ihn ihr.

g Sie verkaufen ihn dir.

Remember that in German accusative pronouns come before dative pronouns.

Remember that pronouns change case just like the nouns they replace. Subject pronouns are in the nominative, direct object pronouns are in the accusative and indirect object pronouns are in the dative. For example: *ich* = I, *mich* = me and *mir* = to me.

2 In the sentences below, the direct object pronouns are circled and the indirect object pronouns are underlined. Write the equivalent English word in the brackets.

a Meine Mutter hat immer Zeit für (mich) (*me*) und ich kann mit ihr (*her*) über alles reden.

b Ich finde (sie) (................) aber ziemlich streng, weil sie mir (................) kein Taschengeld gibt.

c Ich verstehe mich gut mit meinem Vater und es freut (mich) (................), Zeit mit ihm (................) zu verbringen.

d Meine Eltern unterstützen (mich) (................) und ich verstehe mich sehr gut mit ihnen (................).

e Meine Schwester ist sehr nett, also verbringe ich viel Zeit mit ihr (................).

3 The sentences below all use the pronoun *sie* or *Sie*. Using the context, work out the meaning of each *sie* or *Sie*, write it in the brackets and explain your choice on the line.

a Ich habe eine Schwester. Sie (*she*) ist vierzehn Jahre alt.

subject pronoun, referring back to sister

b Ich verstehe mich gut mit meiner Mutter. Ich finde sie (................) sehr nett.

....

c Ich wohne bei meinen Eltern. Sie (................) heißen Barbara und Roland.

....

d Ich mache nicht gern Wintersportarten, denn ich finde sie (................) gefährlich.

....

e Woher kommen Sie (................)?

....

Your turn!

Here is an exam-style question practising the skills you have worked on, in particular how words relate to each other in a sentence, how different verb tenses are used and how pronouns are used.

The text in your exam will not have boxes for you to fill in. They are here to help you practise your skills.

Exam-style question

Friendship

Read the conversation in a German chat room between three teenagers about their best friends.

Meine beste Freundin heißt Lotte. Sie hat lange, blonde Haare und braune Augen und sie ist sehr schlank. Unser Lieblingshobby ist Leichtathletik – wir sind sehr gute Athletinnen und müssen dreimal pro Woche trainieren. Lotte und ich sind beste Freundinnen, denn ich kann mit ihr über alles reden. Letztes Wochenende sind wir zusammen ins Kino gegangen und wir haben dort eine Komödie gesehen. In den Sommerferien fahren wir nach Spanien. Ich freue mich darauf! **Sabine**

Als ich klein war ☐, spielte ☐ ich oft mit meiner Freundin im Garten. Wir sind ☐ immer noch Freunde, obwohl ich in Berlin wohne ☐ und sie in Köln wohnt ☐. Wir sehen ☐ uns nicht oft, aber wir skypen einmal pro Woche. Am Wochenende werde ich nach Köln fahren ☐ und wir werden zusammen ins Konzert gehen ☐. Wir sind große Fans von Tokio Hotel. **Thomas**

Ich ☐ kenne meine Freundin seit drei Jahren. Sie ☐ heißt Jenny und ich habe sie ☐ in England kennengelernt, weil sie ☐ meine Austauschpartnerin war. Letzten Sommer habe ich eine Woche bei ihr ☐ in London verbracht und das hat viel Spaß gemacht. Dieses Jahr wird Jenny eine Woche bei mir ☐ zu Hause verbringen. Ich ☐ werde viel Sport mit Jenny treiben. **Kim**

1. For Sabine, highlight or circle the subject, verb and object in different colours.
2. For Thomas, indicate which tense is being used by writing **P** for past, **Pr** for present and **F** for future in the boxes.
3. For Kim, indicate the type of pronoun by writing **D** for direct object pronouns, **I** for indirect object pronouns and **S** for subject pronouns.
4. Now complete the exam-style question.

Exam-style question

Write **four** correct activities in the table.

	Past	Present	Future
Sabine	*cinema to see a comedy*	*athletics*	*going to Spain on holiday*
Thomas	*garden play with friend*		
Kim		*friend is called Jenny*	

(4 marks)

Your turn!

Here is a second exam-style question, which requires you to practise the skills you have worked on. Use the checklist below to help you.

Exam-style question

My perfect wedding

Your German friend Isa is describing her perfect wedding.

In der Zukunft möchte ich heiraten, aber ich möchte keine große Party organisieren, weil ich sie sehr teuer finde. Eine kleinere, billigere Hochzeit finde ich besser. Ich werde nicht in einer Kirche heiraten, denn ich möchte lieber am Strand heiraten. Meine Schwester hat im Ausland geheiratet, aber das werde ich nicht machen. Meiner Meinung nach ist es besser, in Deutschland zu heiraten.

Das Brautkleid ist mir sehr wichtig und ich werde schöne Dekorationen kaufen und Blumen bestellen. Ich werde keinen Fotograf einstellen, weil meine Gäste Fotos machen werden. Ich werde kein Hochzeitsauto buchen, weil mein Bruder uns fahren kann. Er hat einen weißen Mercedes-Benz.

Das Hochzeitsmenü ist mir sehr wichtig, aber ich möchte keine große Hochzeitstorte auswählen. Ich esse nicht gern Kuchen! Wir werden lieber Schokoladeneis essen.

What is Isa **not** planning to do for her wedding? List **six** things.

1 ....

2 ....

3 ....

4 ....

5 ....

6 ....

(6 marks)

Checklist Before I give my answers, have I ...	✓
identified the subject, verb and object in each sentence?	
understood different verb tenses?	
understood subject pronouns?	
understood the difference between direct and indirect object pronouns?	
recognised the different meanings of *sie* and *Sie*?	

Remember to use the word order to help you work out which is the subject and which is the object. Look at the words highlighted in yellow and decide which is which.

You should also look at the different tenses being used and remember to use time phrases and other context clues to help you. Look at the words highlighted in pink and think about which tenses are being used.

Review your skills

Check up

Review your response to the exam-style questions on pages 23 and 24. Tick ✓ the column to show how well you think you have done each of the following.

	Not quite ✓	Nearly there ✓	Got it! ✓
understood how words relate to each other in a sentence	☐	☐	☐
understood different verb tenses	☐	☐	☐
understood pronouns	☐	☐	☐

Need more practice?

Go back to pages 18 and 19 and do the exam-style questions there.

Top tips to help you understand German texts:

1. Understand how words relate to each other in a sentence.
2. Analyse each sentence before trying to answer the questions.
3. Look out for:
   - Subject
   - Verb
   - Object
   - Tense
   - Pronouns

How confident do you feel about each of these **skills**? Colour in the bars.

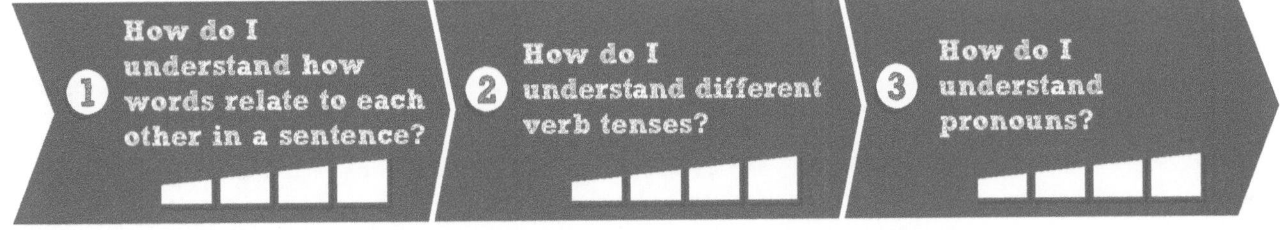

1 How do I understand how words relate to each other in a sentence?
2 How do I understand different verb tenses?
3 How do I understand pronouns?

Identifying information that is relevant to the question

This unit will help you identify the information that is needed to answer the question. The skills you will build are to:

- ensure that you don't take information out of context
- avoid relying too much on individual words
- understand question words.

In the exam, you will be asked to tackle reading exercises like the two on these pages. This unit will help you learn skills to respond to this type of exam question.

Do not answer this question yet. You will be asked to come back to it at the end of the unit.

Exam-style question

In a literary text, you may not understand all the vocabulary, some of which might not be in the minimum core vocabulary list.

Ein Haus voller Bücher

Lies diesen Auszug aus dem Buch *Tintenherz* von Cornelia Funke.

Beantworte die Fragen auf **Deutsch**.

Überall in ihrem Haus stapelten sich Bücher. Sie standen nicht nur in Regalen wie bei anderen Leuten, nein, bei ihnen stapelten sie sich unter den Tischen, auf Stühlen, in den Zimmerecken. Es gab sie in der Küche und auf dem Klo, auf dem Fernseher und im Kleiderschrank, kleine Stapel, hohe Stapel, dicke, dünne, alte, neue … Bücher. Sie empfingen Meggie mit einladend aufgeschlagenen Seiten auf dem Frühstückstisch, trieben grauen Tagen die Langeweile aus – und manchmal stolperte man über sie.

1 Was stand unter den Tischen?

....

(1 mark)

2 In welchem Zimmer gab es Bücher?

....

(1 mark)

3 Wer liest beim Frühstück?

....

(1 mark)

4 Was passiert manchmal mit den Büchern?

....

(1 mark)

The imperfect is often used in literary texts and also appears in other texts in this unit. It is important to make sure you know how this tense works for regular verbs and that you have also looked over irregular verbs.

Get started

Do not answer this question yet. You will be asked to come back to it at the end of the unit.

Exam-style question

Auf Austausch

Lies diesen Text über einen Austausch nach Deutschland.

Beantworte die Fragen auf **Deutsch**.

> Meine Austauschpartnerin Susi wohnt in einem großen Haus auf dem Land. Das ist ein Einfamilienhaus und es ist größer als mein Haus. Es gibt einen kleinen Garten vor dem Haus und einen größeren Garten hinter dem Haus. Die Mutter von Susi arbeitet gern im Garten.
>
> Im Erdgeschoss gibt es ein Wohnzimmer mit Essecke und eine große Küche. Im ersten Stock gibt es vier Schlafzimmer, ein Badezimmer und ein Klo. Im Dachboden gibt es sogar einen Spieleraum und ein Arbeitszimmer. Ihr Vater arbeitet zu Hause, weil er Schriftsteller ist.
>
> Als ich bei Susi wohnte, habe ich mit ihr ein Zimmer geteilt. Als ich bei ihr wohnte, mussten wir um sieben Uhr aufstehen, weil die Schule sehr früh anfing. Am Nachmittag nach der Schule mussten wir leise sein, weil ihr Vater arbeiten musste. **Luisa**

1 In was für einem Haus wohnt Susi?

....

(1 mark)

2 Wer arbeitet oft im Garten?

....

(1 mark)

3 Wo schlief Luisa, als sie bei Susi wohnte?

....

(1 mark)

4 Warum mussten die Mädchen nach der Schule ruhig bleiben?

....

(1 mark)

The three key questions in the **skills boosts** will help you identify information that is needed to answer the question.

How do I ensure that I don't take information out of context?

How do I avoid relying too much on individual words?

How do I understand question words?

1 How do I ensure that I don't take information out of context?

Before attempting the questions on a text, skim-read and summarise in one sentence what the text is about to understand the general context. Then try breaking down the text into self-contained chunks with their own contexts to help you answer the questions.

1 Skim-read through the exam-style question text on page 26, then tick the correct statement summarising what the text is about.

The text is about:

- a what Meggie's house looks like ☐
- b books in Meggie's house ☐
- c the location of Meggie's house ☐

The context of the text is the general setting or background. Understanding the general context of a text will help you understand the meaning of individual parts of the text.

When skim-reading a text, ask yourself the following questions:
- What clues are contained in the title?
- What clues are contained in the rubric?
- Are there any key dates, days or times?
- Which words or phrases are repeated?
- What is the first sentence in each paragraph?

2 The same stimulus text is set out in five chunks in the left-hand column below. Draw lines to match each chunk with one of the contexts listed on the right.

- **A** Überall in ihrem Haus stapelten sich Bücher. Sie standen nicht nur in Regalen wie bei anderen Leuten, nein, bei ihnen stapelten sie sich unter den Tischen, auf Stühlen, in den Zimmerecken.
- **B** Es gab sie in der Küche und auf dem Klo, auf dem Fernseher und im Kleiderschrank,
- **C** kleine Stapel, hohe Stapel, dicke, dünne, alte, neue … Bücher.
- **D** Sie empfingen Meggie mit einladend aufgeschlagenen Seiten auf dem Frühstückstisch, trieben grauen Tagen die Langeweile aus
- **E** und manchmal stolperte man über sie.

- **a** Which rooms the books are in
- **b** Why and when Meggie reads
- **c** A problem caused by the books
- **d** Where exactly the books are
- **e** What sort of books there are

3 Link the chunks from 2 to the questions below by writing the letter of the relevant chunk in each box. There are four questions here and five chunks.

- a Was stand unter den Tischen? ☐
- b In welchem Zimmer gab es Bücher? ☐
- c Wer liest beim Frühstück? ☐
- d Was passiert manchmal mit den Büchern? ☐

Remember that the questions will be in the order of the text.

How do I avoid relying too much on individual words?

When faced with an unfamiliar word, a key strategy is to work out its meaning from the phrase or sentence it is in. Look at the words surrounding the unfamiliar word and then make a reasonable guess about the meaning of the unfamiliar word from the context.

? What type of word is the unfamiliar word? (noun, verb, adjective, adverb, connective, etc.)

? Where is the action taking place?

? Who/What is doing the action?

? What is my best reasonable guess as to the meaning of the unfamiliar word?

1 Read the sentences below. The words in bold might be unfamiliar. Annotate the words around them.

> Annotating the words around an unfamiliar word can help to identify the type of word and what it might mean.

stood in

a Die Bücher standen in **Regalen**.

b Bei ihnen **stapelten** sie **sich** unter den Tischen, auf Stühlen und in den **Zimmerecken**.

c Als ich bei ihr wohnte, mussten wir um sieben Uhr aufstehen, weil die Schule sehr **früh** anfing.

d Im Erdgeschoss gibt es ein Wohnzimmer mit **Essecke** und eine große Küche.

e Im ersten Stock gibt es vier Schlafzimmer, ein Badezimmer und ein **Klo**.

f Als ich bei Susi wohnte, habe ich mit ihr ein Zimmer **geteilt**.

2 A student has translated the sentence below, substituting the unfamiliar words (shown here in bold) with question marks. They have then written a brief summary of the sentence in English.

> When faced with a sentence with several unfamiliar words, it can be helpful to have a go at translating the whole sentence and seeing what you **can** understand, despite not understanding every word.

Es gab sie in der Küche und auf dem **Klo**, auf dem Fernseher und im **Kleiderschrank**, kleine **Stapel**, hohe **Stapel**, dicke, **dünne**, alte, neue … Bücher.

They were in the kitchen and on the ?, on the TV and in the ?, small ?, high ?,

thick, ?, old, new … books.

This sentence is about books being everywhere in the house.

Using the same technique, translate and summarise the following short extract.

Im **Dachboden** gibt es **sogar** einen **Spieleraum** und ein Arbeitszimmer. Ihr Vater arbeitet zu Hause, weil er **Schriftsteller** ist.

....

....

....

3 How do I understand question words?

It is important to identify and understand the question words most commonly used in reading comprehension questions.

1 Draw lines to match the questions below with their English meanings.

A Wann wohnte Luisa im Haus?	a What was the house like?
B Warum wohnte Luisa im Haus?	b Where was the house?
C Was stand vor dem Haus?	c Who lived in the house?
D Welche Personen wohnten im Haus?	d Why was Luisa living in the house?
E Wer wohnte im Haus?	e Which people lived in the house?
F Wie war das Haus?	f What stood in front of the house?
G Wo war das Haus?	g When did Luisa live in the house?

Understanding the meaning of the 'big seven' question words below can be extremely helpful in working out what questions are being asked. Watch out for *wer* and *wo* which are 'false friends'.

wann = when	*was* = what	*wie* = how
warum = why	*wer* = who	*wo* = where

welcher/welche/welches = which (changes gender depending on the subject)

2 On paper, translate the following questions into English.

a Was stand unter den Tischen?

b In welchem Zimmer gab es Bücher?

c Wer liest beim Frühstück?

d Was passiert manchmal mit den Büchern?

3 Some of the 'big seven' question words combine with other words to form different questions. Draw lines to match the questions below with the correct answers.

Learn these combined question words:
was für = what kind of
wie lange = how long
wie viel(e) = how much/how many

A Was für Bücher gab es im Haus?	a Sie wohnte zwei Wochen dort.
B Wie lange wohnte Luisa im Haus?	b Es gab zehn Zimmer.
C Wie viele Zimmer gab es?	c Es gab dicke, dünne, alte, neue Bücher.

4 Write the missing question word to complete each of the questions below.

a .... kommst du?
Ich komme aus England.

b .... stand das Buch?
Es stand auf dem Tisch.

c .... schreibst du?
Ich schreibe mit einem Kuli.

d .... fährst du?
Ich fahre nach Berlin.

Wo is a very flexible question word which can combine with other words, often prepositions, to form a range of question words.
woher = where from
wohin = where to
womit = what with
worauf = on what
worin = in what

Your turn!

Here is an exam-style question which requires you to practise the skills you have worked on, in particular how to identify context, deal with unfamiliar words and select information relevant to the question.

Exam-style question

Anton ist weg

Lies diesen Auszug aus dem Buch *Pünktchen und Anton*, geschrieben von Erich Kästner.

Beantworte die Fragen auf **Deutsch**.

Sie begann ihn zu suchen, sie trat ins Schlafzimmer. Sie ging in die Küche. Sie sah sogar in der Toilette nach. Sie machte im Korridor Licht und schaute hinter die Schränke. ‚Anton!' rief sie. ‚Komm, mein Junge, ich bin wieder gut! Anton!'

Sie rief bald laut und bald leise und zärtlich. Er war nicht in der Wohnung. Er war fortgelaufen! Sie wurde sehr unruhig. Sie rief bittend seinen Namen. Er war fort.

Er war fort! Da riss sie die Wohnungstür auf und rannte die Treppe hinunter, ihren Jungen suchen.

1 Was begann die Mutter von Anton zu machen?

....

(1 mark)

2 Wie fühlte sich die Mutter von Anton?

....

(1 mark)

3 Wo war Anton?

....

(1 mark)

4 Was hat die Mutter von Anton gemacht, nachdem sie die Tür geöffnet hat?

....

(1 mark)

① Summarise the text in the exam-style question in one sentence. ....

....

② Divide the text into four chunks using different coloured highlighters and briefly write the general context of each chunk on paper.

③ Work out the meanings of the question words *was*, *wie* and *wo* from questions 1–4 above. Then match the four highlighted chunks of text with the relevant questions by writing the question numbers in the boxes below. It may be that one chunk is not relevant to any question, while another is relevant to more than one question.

a ☐ b ☐ c ☐ d ☐

④ Now write your answers to the exam-style question above.

Your turn!

Now answer the following exam-style question which requires you to practise the skills you have worked on, in particular how to identify information that is relevant to the question. Use the checklist below to help you.

Exam-style question

Mein Zuhause

Lies den Text.

Beantworte die Fragen auf **Deutsch**.

Als ich klein war, wohnte ich in einem Wohnblock in Berlin. Ich wohnte gern dort, weil meine Freunde in der Nähe wohnten und wir nicht weit von der Schule wohnten.

Vor fünf Jahren sind wir umgezogen und wir wohnen seitdem in einem Einfamilienhaus in einem ruhigen Stadtviertel. Das Haus ist ziemlich modern und groß und es gefällt mir, mein eigenes Zimmer zu haben. Früher musste ich leider ein Zimmer mit meinem Bruder teilen.

Ein Nachteil ist, dass ich jetzt mit dem Zug und dann mit dem Bus zur Schule fahren muss. Ich muss also sehr früh aufstehen, sonst komme ich zu spät.

In der Zukunft möchte ich in London oder in den Vereinigten Staaten wohnen. Mein Traum ist es, in einem Wolkenkratzer* mit einer Rolltreppe und einem Aufzug zu wohnen. Meiner Meinung nach wäre das prima. **Mathias**

* *der Wolkenkratzer* = skyscraper

1 Wo wohnte Mathias, als er jünger war?

....

(1 mark)

2 Seit wann wohnt er in einem Einfamilienhaus?

....

(1 mark)

3 Warum muss er sehr früh aufstehen?

....

(1 mark)

4 In was für einem Haus/einer Wohnung möchte er wohnen?

....

(1 mark)

Checklist **Before I give my answers, have I …**	✓
understood the general context of the text?	
understood the context of each chunk of the text?	
used underlining/highlighting if necessary to help me understand?	
used my knowledge of the context, vocabulary and grammar to work out the meaning of unfamiliar words?	
understood the exam questions?	

Review your skills

Check up

Review your response to the exam-style questions on pages 31 and 32. Tick the column to show how well you think you have done each of the following.

	Not quite	Nearly there	Got it!
ensured that I haven't taken information out of context	☐	☐	☐
avoided relying too much on individual words	☐	☐	☐
understood question words	☐	☐	☐

Need more practice?

Go back to pages 26 and 27 and do the exam-style questions there.

Top tips to help you use prepositions as a key to meaning:

1. Understanding prepositions (e.g. 'in', 'under', 'on') can often unlock the meaning of a text and questions.
2. Make sure you understand any prepositions in the particular context of the text or questions.
3. Look back over the texts in this unit and make a list of the prepositions, the context, and their English meanings.

How confident do you feel about each of these **skills**? Colour in the bars.

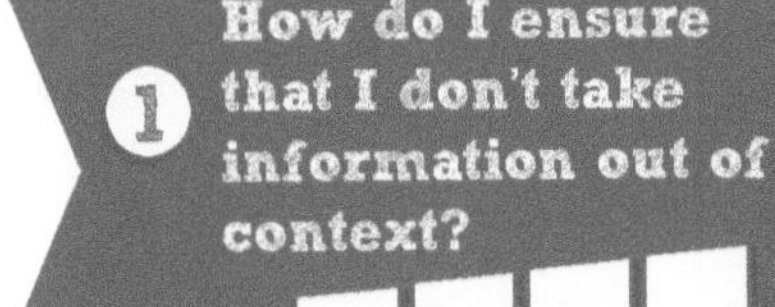
1
How do I ensure that I don't take information out of context?

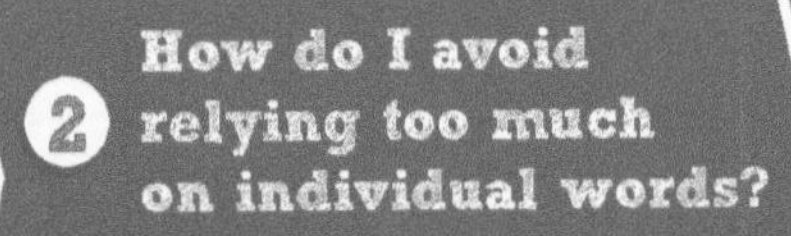
2
How do I avoid relying too much on individual words?

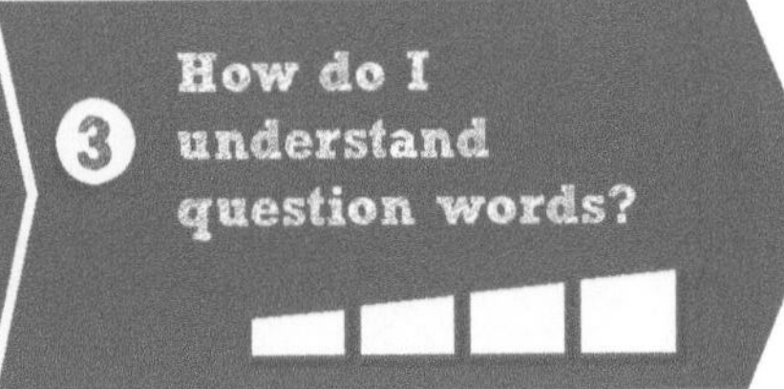
3
How do I understand question words?

5 Expressing the answer clearly and with appropriate detail

This unit will help you to write clear and detailed full sentences. The skills you will build are to:

- avoid ambiguity and contradiction in your answers
- ensure that your answers are sufficiently detailed
- avoid including irrelevant information.

In the exam, you will be asked to tackle reading exercises like the two on these pages. This unit will prepare you to respond to these types of exam questions.

This is a literary text. Remember that literary texts often use the imperfect tense, so it would be helpful to look back over the regular verb endings.

Also review the irregular forms of the imperfect: words like *war* and *gab* don't use the regular verb endings but will be used in texts.

Do not answer this question yet. You will be asked to come back to it at the end of the unit.

Exam-style question

Lies diesen Text aus dem Buch *Zeitenzauber – Die magische Gondel* von Eva Völler über die Sommerferien von Anna.

Beantworte die Fragen auf **Deutsch**.

Wir aßen wie üblich im Restaurant neben dem Hotel zu Abend. Mama meinte, in ganz Venedig gebe es keine bessere Pasta. Mir persönlich gefiel das Restaurant schon deshalb, weil es in Reichweite* vom WLAN-Anschluss des Hotels lag und ich zwischen Antipasti und Hauptgang im Internet surfen konnte.

„Weißt du, manchmal könntest du etwas mehr Interesse zeigen, wenn dein Vater von seiner Arbeit erzählt", sagte Mama, als Papa nach der Vorspeise kurz zum Telefonieren hinausging. „Sein Beruf ist für ihn sehr wichtig!"

„Aber ich zeige doch Interesse", behauptete ich. „Ich höre immer zu!"

„Und spielst dabei unterm Tisch mit deinem Handy herum."

„Es ist kein Handy, sondern ein iPod Touch", sagte ich lahm.

* *in Reichweite* = within range/reach

1 Wo waren Anna und ihre Eltern?

....

(1 mark)

2 Warum fand Anna das Restaurant gut?

....

(1 mark)

3 Wer telefonierte?

....

(1 mark)

4 Was machte Anna unter dem Tisch?

....

(1 mark)

Get started

In addition to answering questions in German, you will also have to answer questions in English.
The exam-style question below is an example of this type of question.

Do not answer this question yet. You will be asked to come back to it at the end of the unit.

Exam-style question

Problems!

Your German friend, Axel, writes to discuss problems he had on a recent school trip.

Answer the questions in **English**.

Hallo!

Letzte Woche bin ich mit der Schule nach Berlin gefahren. Am Morgen mussten wir ins Museum gehen und dann haben wir Freizeit in der Stadtmitte gehabt. Meine Freunde und ich haben viele Probleme gehabt.

Zuerst haben wir uns verlaufen und mussten einen Polizisten nach dem Weg fragen. Danach sind wir ins Restaurant gegangen, aber das Essen war kalt uns es war ein Haar in meinem Salat. Pfui! Mir war sehr schlecht.

Am Nachmittag sind wir einkaufen gegangen, aber mein Freund Oskar hat sein Geld verloren. Wir mussten zur Polizeiwache gehen, um das zu melden. Danach ist mein Handy aus meiner Tasche gefallen und es ist jetzt total kaputt. Meine Mutter war nicht zufrieden!

1 What did the boys have to do in the morning?

....

(1 mark)

2 How did Axel feel after the meal?

....

(1 mark)

3 Why did they go to the police station?

....

(1 mark)

The three key questions in the skills boosts will help you write clear and detailed full sentences.

How do I avoid ambiguity and contradiction in my answers?

How do I ensure that my answers are sufficiently detailed?

How do I avoid including irrelevant information?

1 How do I avoid ambiguity and contradiction in my answers?

In order to avoid ambiguity when answering in full sentences, you need to check that your answers make sense, paying particular attention to verb endings and tenses.

Remember:

- Look for the verb and tense in the question and use the same verb and tense in your answer.
- Look for the subject in the question and use the same person of the verb in your answer.
- You will need to change the order of the subject and verb to keep the verb as the second idea of the sentence.

You can re-use the subject or object as it is given in the question, or replace it with a pronoun. For example:

Anna = *sie* (she) *Axel* = *er* (he) *Das Essen* = *es* (it) *Anna und ihre Eltern* = *sie* (they)

1 Complete the following four steps for each question below.

i Decide which tense is used. Write 'I' for imperfect and 'P' for present in the box.

ii The verb and subject have been highlighted. Use them to start an answer. You don't need to complete the answers at this point.

iii Look at the question word and the other words in the sentence. Annotate how you would continue, using a noun, verb, adjective, connective, time phrase or other type of word.

iv Repeat step ii on paper, this time replacing the subject with a pronoun.

a Wann war Axel in Berlin? I

Axel war / + time phrase + in Berlin / Er war ...

b Warum fand Anna das Restaurant gut?

c Wie ist das Essen?

d Wo war das Haar?

e Wie lange waren Axel und seine Freunde in Berlin?

f Was für eine Person ist Anna?

Some questions require a different approach:

- *Wer* and *welch(e)*: answer includes name/object
- *Was* + verb: answer includes verb
- *Wie viel(e)*: answer includes number

2 Make notes showing how you might answer the questions below.

a Wer wohnte im Haus? *name + wohnte im Haus.*

b Welche Personen wohnen im Hotel?

c Was machte Anna unter dem Tisch?

d Wie viele Personen sind im Hotel?

2 How do I ensure that my answers are sufficiently detailed?

In order to include sufficient detail you need to check that you have included all relevant information from the text.

You first need to identify exactly what information is required to answer each question.

1 Translate the questions below into English. Then underline the key information you will need to find in the text.

a Wo waren Anna und ihre Eltern?

Where were Anna and her parents?

b Warum fand Anna das Restaurant gut?

c Wer telefonierte?

d Was machte Anna unter dem Tisch?

2 A student has identified the sections in the text, given below, which are relevant to answer each of the questions you translated and underlined in 1. Underline the specific information needed to answer the questions. Translate it into English to be sure it answers the questions.

a Wir aßen wie üblich im Restaurant neben dem Hotel zu Abend.

in the restaurant next to the hotel

b Mir persönlich gefiel das Restaurant schon deshalb, weil es in Reichweite vom WLAN-Anschluss des Hotels lag und ich zwischen Antipasti und Hauptgang im Internet surfen konnte.

c als Papa nach der Vorspeise kurz zum Telefonieren hinausging

d „Und spielst dabei unterm Tisch mit deinem Handy herum."
„Es ist kein Handy, sondern ein iPod Touch", sagte ich lahm.

Make sure you have scanned the whole text to be sure you have missed no relevant details. For example, if you are looking for mentions of locations, scan the whole text to make sure you have correctly highlighted every sentence where a location is mentioned and then check whether each location is relevant to the question.

3 How do I avoid including irrelevant information?

In order to avoid including irrelevant information, you need to check you don't answer a different question from the one asked. Before answering a question, look carefully at the number of marks. If there is only one mark, then you will need to provide one piece of information, so make sure you know exactly which piece of information is relevant by translating the question word.

1 Look at the questions and answers below. Circle (A) the question word in each question. Then underline (A) the detail in each answer which does **not** specifically answer that question.

Including extra irrelevant information can cost you marks in the exam, especially if you make grammatical mistakes in the extra information.

The question word here is *wann*, so you only need to mention **when** he is going to Berlin, not **how**.

a Wann fährt er nach Berlin?

Er fährt am Samstag mit dem Zug nach Berlin.

b Warum fährt er nach Berlin?

Er fährt am Samstag nach Berlin, um seine Freunde zu besuchen.

c Was hat sie gekauft?

Sie hat ein T-Shirt im Kleidungsgeschäft gekauft.

d Welchen Rock trägt sie heute Abend?

Sie trägt den schwarzen Rock, denn er ist sehr hübsch.

e Wer fährt mit ihr?

Ihr Bruder fährt mit ihr, weil er sehr lustig ist.

f Wie war die Reise?

Die Reise war sehr lang und er hat ein Buch gelesen.

g Wo liegt die Jugendherberge?

Die Jugendherberge liegt in der Altstadt und ist sehr groß und modern.

2 Look at the answers in English to the following questions and underline (A) the part of each sentence that is directly relevant to the question asked.

a What did the boys have to do in the morning?

In the morning, they had to go to the museum and then they had free time in the town centre.

b How did Axel feel after the meal?

The food was cold and Axel had a hair in his salad. He felt very sick.

c Why did they go to the police station?

In the afternoon they went shopping, but Oskar lost his money. They had to go to the police station to report it.

It is important to follow the same advice when answering in full sentences in German and in English, as similar mistakes can occur. Make sure you've identified which question is being asked, have avoided grammatical errors and have not lifted whole sections from the text, even if you have translated these correctly into English.

Your turn!

Here is an exam-style question which requires you to practise the skills you have worked on, in particular how to avoid ambiguity and include sufficient detail.

Exam-style question

Lies diesen Text aus dem Buch *Marsmädchen* von Tamara Bach über die Stadt von Miriam.

Beantworte die Fragen auf **Deutsch**.

> Die Stadt, in der ich wohne, ist hübsch und klein, im Sommer kommen Touristen, um sich die Kirche und die alte Burg* anzuschauen und durch die alten Gassen zu spazieren. Im Sommer ist es hier schön. Man kann auf einem Feld sitzen, ins Tal schauen und sich mit jemandem eine Flasche Wein teilen, vielleicht ist es dann Abend. Man kann an den Baggersee fahren, wenn es Tag ist, oder ins Schwimmbad einbrechen, wenn es Nacht ist. Man muss gar nicht viel im Sommer machen, um etwas zu machen. Im Sommer reicht es, wenn man einfach da ist. Egal wo.

* *die Burg* = castle

1 Wie ist die Stadt von Miriam?

....

(1 mark)

2 Was gibt es im Sommer für Touristen?

....

(1 mark)

3 Wo kann man im Sommer sitzen?

....

(1 mark)

4 Was kann man an einem Sommertag machen?

....

(1 mark)

1. Highlight the verb and subject in each question and use them to begin your answer, remembering to change the order. Pink has been used in the example above.
2. Using a different colour (yellow in the example above), highlight the question word in each question and consider what details you need to include in the rest of your answer. Decide whether you need nouns, verbs, adjectives, connectives or other types of words.
3. Using a third colour (green in the example above), highlight the details in the text relevant to each question.
4. Now complete your answer to each question.

Your turn!

Here is a second exam-style question which requires you to practise the skills you have worked on, in particular how to write clear, detailed and unambiguous answers.

Exam-style question

Shopping

Your German exchange partner, Ava, describes a recent shopping trip.

Answer the questions in **English**.

> Hallo!
>
> Meine Mutter hatte am Wochenende Geburtstag und wir mussten ein Geschenk für sie kaufen. Meine Schwester und ich sind zusammen einkaufen gegangen.
>
> Zuerst sind wir zum Warenhaus gegangen, aber meine Schwester hat nichts gefunden. Das Kleid war „zu altmodisch", die Bluse war „zu eng" und der Rock war „zu groß".
>
> Zum Schluss (drei Stunden später) sind wir ins Schreibwarengeschäft gegangen. Wir haben dort für unsere Mutter einen bunten Kuli, ein Fotoalbum, eine Duftkerze und ein schönes Notizbuch gekauft. Das nächste Mal werde ich ohne meine Schwester einkaufen gehen. Sie ist sehr nervig!

1 Why did Ava and her sister go shopping together?

....

(1 mark)

2 Name one thing the girls bought.

....

(1 mark)

3 How does Ava feel about shopping with her sister?

....

(1 mark)

① Identify and highlight the section of text which is relevant to each question.

② Within the sections you have highlighted, underline the specific information needed to answer the questions.

③ Now write your answers to the exam-style question, using the checklist to help you.

Checklist **Before I give my answers, have I ...**	✓
looked for the verb and tense in the questions?	
checked the tenses I've used in my answers?	
included all relevant details by matching the question words with specific information from the text?	
avoided including details which answer a different question?	
avoided lifting whole sections of text?	

Review your skills

Check up

Review your response to the exam-style questions on pages 39 and 40. Tick the column to show how well you think you have done each of the following.

	Not quite	Nearly there	Got it!
avoided ambiguity and contradiction in my answers	☐	☐	☐
ensured that my answers are sufficiently detailed	☐	☐	☐
avoided including irrelevant information	☐	☐	☐

Need more practice?

Go back to pages 34 and 35 and do the exam-style questions there.

Top tips to help you handle dialogue in texts:

When reading literary texts, you may encounter a variety of phrases used to describe what people say or think. Make sure you recognise and understand these.

Typical dialogue phrases include:

Mama meinte ...	Mum said ...
... behauptete ich	... I claimed
laut meiner Schwester	according to my sister

Similarly, phrases to describe what people think include:

Meiner Meinung nach ...	In my opinion ...
Ich dachte ...	I thought ...
Meine Schwester fand ...	My sister found ...

How confident do you feel about each of these **skills**? Colour in the bars.

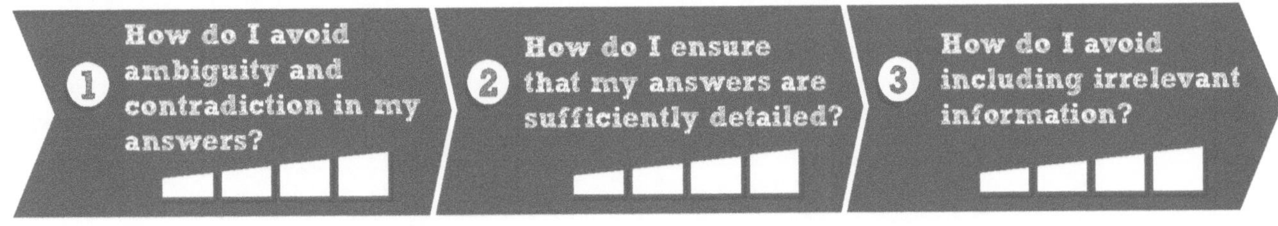
1 How do I avoid ambiguity and contradiction in my answers?
2 How do I ensure that my answers are sufficiently detailed?
3 How do I avoid including irrelevant information?

Get started

6 Spotting synonyms and antonyms

This unit will help you to understand core vocabulary, especially synonyms and antonyms. The skills you will build are to:

- recognise words that belong to the same topic
- recognise synonyms and near-synonyms
- recognise antonyms and near-antonyms.

In the exam, you will be asked to tackle reading exercises like the two on these pages. This unit will prepare you to respond to these types of exam questions. In the exam, you will see rubrics in German and rubrics in English. In this particular question type, the rubrics are in German.

Do not answer this question yet. You will be asked to come back to it at the end of the unit.

Exam-style question

Im Urlaub

Lies den Text und beantworte die Fragen.

Schreib **R**, wenn die Aussage **richtig** ist,

F, wenn die Aussage **falsch** ist,

NT, wenn die Aussage **nicht im Text** ist.

Ich mache nicht gern Aktivurlaub, weil ich nicht sportlich bin. Ich liege gern in der Sonne, also mache ich lieber Strandurlaub in Deutschland. Aber letztes Jahr habe ich trotzdem einen Abenteuerurlaub in Frankreich gemacht. Während des Urlaubs habe ich eine Raftingtour gemacht und ich habe in einem Zelt übernachtet. Das hat mir nicht gefallen, denn das Wetter war so schlecht. Es hat geregnet und gehagelt. Wir haben gefroren! Nächstes Jahr werde ich nicht auf einem Campingplatz übernachten. Ich werde in einem Hotel wohnen und werde mich entspannen. **Tania**

1 Tania ist sehr aktiv. **(1 mark)**

2 In den Ferien macht sie jeden Tag Wassersport. **(1 mark)**

3 Letztes Jahr ist sie ins Ausland gefahren. **(1 mark)**

4 Sie hat auf einem Campingplatz gewohnt. **(1 mark)**

5 Tania war mit den Ferien zufrieden. **(1 mark)**

6 Während der Ferien war es sehr kalt. **(1 mark)**

7 In der Zukunft wird Tania nicht zelten. **(1 mark)**

8 Sie wird sehr aktiv sein. **(1 mark)**

Do not answer this question yet. You will be asked to come back to it at the end of the unit.

Exam-style question

Meine Ferien

Martina ist im Urlaub nach Salzburg gefahren. Lies den Text.

Welche **sechs** Aussagen sind richtig?

Schreib die richtigen Buchstaben in die Kästchen.

Meine Ferien waren entsetzlich! Am ersten Tag sind wir vom Flughafen mit dem Zug weitergefahren. Das Problem war, dass wir in die falsche Richtung gefahren sind! Wir mussten aus dem Zug aussteigen und haben dann eine Stunde lang auf den nächsten Zug gewartet.

Als wir an der Jugendherberge angekommen sind, haben wir Probleme mit unserer Reservierung gehabt. Wir hatten ein Doppelzimmer reserviert, aber wir mussten ein Zimmer mit zehn anderen Personen teilen. Eine Person war sehr laut und wir konnten nicht schlafen. Die Heizung war kaputt und wir konnten in der Jugendherberge nicht essen. Wir mussten also jeden Abend ins Restaurant gehen und das war sehr teuer.

Das Wetter war schrecklich, weil es jeden Tag nass und kalt war. Wir wollten in den Bergen wandern gehen, aber das war unmöglich, denn es war sehr neblig. Nächsten August werde ich nach Spanien fahren und werde dort einen Strandurlaub machen. Dieses Jahr fehlten mir die Sonne, das Meer und das Schwimmbad.

A	Diese Ferien waren für Martina ihre Traumferien.
B	Sie sind nach Österreich geflogen.
C	Sie haben einen Fehler mit dem Zug gemacht.
D	Sie hatten ein Doppelzimmer gebucht.
E	Am Abend war es in der Jugendherberge sehr ruhig.
F	In der Jugendherberge war es zu heiß.
G	Das Essen hat viel Geld gekostet.
H	Das Wetter war nicht gut.
I	Es hat geregnet.
J	Sie haben eine Bergwanderung gemacht.
K	Nächstes Jahr möchte sie an der Küste Ferien machen.
L	Sie schwimmt nicht gern.

☐ ☐ ☐ ☐ ☐ ☐

(6 marks)

The three key questions in the **skills boosts** will help you recognise and understand core vocabulary, especially synonyms and antonyms.

How do I recognise words that belong to the same topic?

How do I understand synonyms and near-synonyms?

How do I understand antonyms and near-antonyms?

How do I recognise words that belong to the same topic?

Learning words in groups or categories can be very helpful in identifying which words are relevant to a particular question. For example, if the question is referring to the weather, you can easily identify which is the relevant vocabulary.

1. Complete the table by sorting the words in the box below into the different categories. Then add at least two more German words to each category.

Sonne Aktivurlaub hageln Strandurlaub Zelt regnen frieren
Campingplatz Hotel Abenteuerurlaub Zug Flughafen
Jugendherberge nass kalt Doppelzimmer Reservierung

Types of holiday	Weather	Accommodation	Transport
Aktivurlaub			

2. The words in the table below have been sorted into categories. Choose a title for each category and write it in the table header.

Flughafen	Stunde	Meer	Flugzeug
Restaurant	Jahr	Sonne	Boot
Schwimmbad	Abend	Strand	Auto
Jugendherberge	Monat	Eis essen	Straßenbahn
Hotel	Tag	Sonnenbaden	Fähre

When reading texts, think about which group you would assign different words to. This can really help you to identify exactly which are the relevant words for a particular question. Once you've looked at each question, work out what key piece of information you need to find (weather, transport, accommodation, etc.).

2 How do I understand synonyms and near-synonyms?

It is extremely important to be aware of pairs of words with the same or similar meanings as examination questions may test understanding of synonyms and near-synonyms.

1 Draw lines to match the words on the left with the words on the right. There may be more than one possible match.

A Wassersport	a in einem Zelt übernachten
B Ausland	b Raftingtour
C aktiv	c gefroren
D auf einem Campingplatz wohnen	d sportlich
E zufrieden	e hat mir gefallen
F kalt	f Frankreich

Synonyms are words which have exactly the same meaning, such as *enorm* and *riesig* (= huge). Near-synonyms are words which have a similar meaning, such as *riesig* and *groß*.

2 Complete the table by choosing the correct synonym/near-synonym pair from the box and writing the words in the correct columns.

	Synonym	Near-synonym
a Urlaub	*Ferien*	*Feiertage*
b wolkig		
c Problem		
d Reservierung		
e erschöpft		
f teuer		

~~Feiertage / Ferien~~ Fehler / Schwierigkeit müde / nicht geschlafen bewölkt / neblig
hat viel Geld gekostet / kostspielig Buchung / Bestellung

When looking out for synonyms, beware of 'false friends'. For example, *zunächst* does not mean 'next'.

3 Read this extract from the text on page 43. On paper, write a synonym or near-synonym from the extract to match each of the key words below.

Das Wetter war schrecklich, weil es jeden Tag nass und kalt war. Wir wollten in den Bergen wandern gehen, aber das war unmöglich, denn es war sehr neblig. Nächsten August werde ich nach Spanien fahren und werde dort einen Strandurlaub machen. Dieses Jahr fehlten mir die Sonne, das Meer und das Schwimmbad.

a gar nicht gut
b regnerisch
c nicht heiß
d Wasser
e eine Bergwanderung machen
f das konnten wir nicht machen

3 How do I understand antonyms and near-antonyms?

You need to be able to demonstrate understanding of antonyms – pairs of words with contrasting meanings. They are often used in exam questions, so it is really important to spot them in a text.

An antonym is a word with a directly opposite meaning to another word, such as *groß* and *klein*. A near-antonym is a word which almost has the opposite meaning to another word, such as *sonnig* and *bedeckt* (= overcast).

1 Draw lines to match each word on the left with an antonym or near-antonym on the right.

A entspannen	a faul
B Sommerurlaub	b gewöhnlich*
C sportlich	c zu Hause / in Deutschland
D außergewöhnlich	d Winterurlaub
E im Ausland	e Strandurlaub
F hat mir gefallen	f heiß
G kalt	g aktiv sein
H Aktivurlaub	h ich war nicht zufrieden

* *gewöhnlich* = usual, ordinary

2 Negative constructions can also be used to create antonyms. Add a negative such as *nicht* or *nie* to the phrases below to create their antonym.

a Ich mache gern Aktivurlaub. *Ich mache nicht gern Aktivurlaub.*

b Ich bin sportlich. ....

c Das hat mir gefallen. ....

d Wir konnten gut schlafen. ....

e Wir konnten in der Jugendherberge essen. ....

....

3 a Read the text below and circle all the adjectives.

Just as in English, the prefix *un-* can be added to an adjective or an adverb to create an antonym.

Ich habe sehr schlechte Ferien gehabt. Das Hotel war dreckig und das Schwimmbad war zu kalt. Ich war sehr unglücklich, weil ich sehr gern schwimme. Unser Hotelzimmer war zu klein und der Balkon war gefährlich. Wir konnten auf dem Balkon nicht sitzen, weil wir uns sehr unsicher fühlten. Im Hotel gab es viele Touristen, aber sie waren unfreundlich.

b Write the antonyms of these adjectives below.

gute ....

....

....

Your turn!

Here is an exam-style question which requires you to practise the skills you have worked on, in particular how to recognise synonyms and antonyms and how to group words into categories.

Remember to look for synonyms and antonyms and to match them in the text and exam-style questions.

Exam-style question

Meine Stadt: Bern

Mia spricht über ihre Stadt. Lies den Text und beantworte die Fragen.

Schreib **R**, wenn die Aussage **richtig** ist,

F, wenn die Aussage falsch ist,

NT, wenn die Aussage **nicht im Text** ist.

Ich wohne in Bern. Das ist die Hauptstadt von der Schweiz. Bern ist eine kleine, historische Stadt. Die Altstadt ist sehr schön. Es gibt auch sechs Brücken, die die Altstadt mit der modernen Stadt verbinden. Bern hat auch mehrere Figurenbrunnen, die in der Mitte des 16. Jahrhunderts gebaut wurden.

Ein Nachteil ist, dass die Einkaufsmöglichkeiten sehr schlecht sind. Ich fahre oft irgendwo anders hin, um einkaufen zu gehen. Am Abend ist es nicht sehr lebendig und man kann nicht einfach ausgehen. Ein Vorteil ist, dass es im Sommer sehr warm ist und man in den vielen Freibädern gut schwimmen kann. Man kann auch in der Aare schwimmen. Das ist ein Fluss, der durch Bern fließt. Er ist sehr kalt und fließt sehr schnell, aber das finde ich prima! **Mia**

1 Bern ist nicht sehr groß. **(1 mark)**

2 Bern hat neue und alte Stadtviertel*. **(1 mark)**

3 In Bern kann man Museen** besuchen. **(1 mark)**

4 Bern hat viele tolle Geschäfte. **(1 mark)**

5 Die Stadt hat ein gutes Nachtleben. **(1 mark)**

6 Im Sommer ist es oft heiß. **(1 mark)**

7 Mia schwimmt nie. **(1 mark)**

8 Die Aare ist sehr warm. **(1 mark)**

* *das Stadtviertel* = part of a town/city

** *Museen* = plural of *Museum*

1. Look for synonym and antonym pairs between the text and the statements. Highlight each pair using a different colour. This has been done for the first two statements.
2. Now complete the exam-style question.

If you cannot find a synonym or antonym pair for one of the statements, it may mean that this information is not in the text.

Your turn!

Here is a second exam-style question which requires you to practise the skills you have worked on, in particular how to recognise synonyms and antonyms and how to group words into topic categories. Use the checklist below to help you.

Exam-style question

Meine Stadt: Zürich

Dario spricht über seine Stadt.

Welche **sechs** Aussagen sind richtig? Schreib die richtigen Buchstaben in die Kästchen.

Ich wohne in einer großen, modernen Stadt im Norden von der Schweiz. Sie heißt Zürich. Im Sommer ist es immer sehr warm und sonnig und im Winter ist es immer sehr kalt. Es schneit oft. Als ich klein war, gingen wir oft Ski laufen oder snowboarden.

Ein Vorteil ist, dass wir gute öffentliche Verkehrsmittel haben. Man kann mit der Straßenbahn, mit dem Zug oder mit dem Bus durch die Stadt fahren. Sie sind sauber, ziemlich billig und immer sehr pünktlich.

Ich wohne in einem alten Stadtviertel. Das ist schön, aber unsere Wohnung ist sehr klein und wir haben viele Nachbarn, also ist es oft sehr laut. In der Zukunft möchte ich in einem Dorf wohnen, weil ich gern auf dem Land bin und gern wandern gehe. Wir dürfen in der Wohnung keine Haustiere haben und wenn ich auf dem Land wohne, werde ich einen Hund haben.

A	Dario wohnt in einer Kleinstadt in der Schweiz.
B	Seine Stadt liegt an der Küste.
C	Das ist eine sehr schmutzige Stadt.
D	Im Sommer ist das Wetter sehr schön.
E	Im Winter geht er oft Ski laufen.
F	Er kann einfach durch die Stadt fahren.
G	Die öffentlichen Verkehrsmittel kommen selten mit Verspätung*.
H	Er wohnt in einem modernen Wohnblock.
I	Sein Stadtviertel ist nicht sehr ruhig.
J	In der Zukunft wird er nicht in der Stadt wohnen.
K	Dario geht nicht gern spazieren.
L	In der Zukunft möchte er ein Haustier haben.

☐ ☐ ☐ ☐ ☐ ☐ **(6 marks)**

* *die Verspätung* = delay

Checklist **Before I give my answers, have I ...**	✓
read the introduction to the question to understand the context and predict the vocabulary?	
read through the text *and* the questions or statements?	
looked for synonyms?	
looked for antonyms?	
identified sets of words that belong to the same topic?	

Review your skills

Check up

Review your response to the exam-style questions on pages 47 and 48. Tick ✓ the column to show how well you think you have done each of the following.

	Not quite ✓	Nearly there ✓	Got it! ✓
recognised words that belong to the same topic	☐	☐	☐
understood synonyms and near-synonyms	☐	☐	☐
understood antonyms and near-antonyms	☐	☐	☐

Need more practice?

Go back to pages 42 and 43 and do ✎ the exam-style questions there.

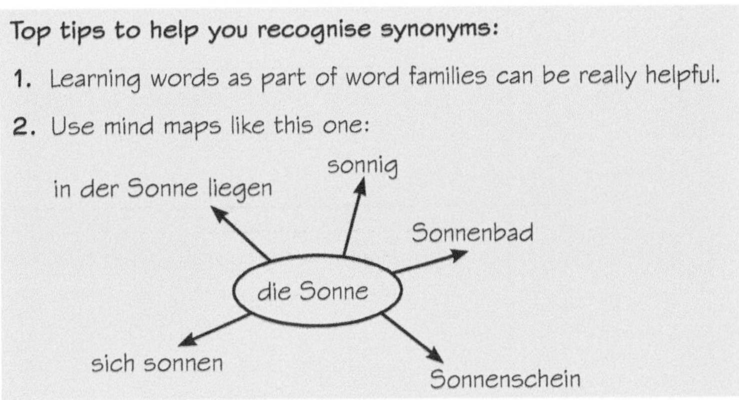

Top tips to help you recognise synonyms:
1. Learning words as part of word families can be really helpful.
2. Use mind maps like this one:
die Sonne
in der Sonne liegen
sonnig
Sonnenbad
sich sonnen
Sonnenschein

How confident do you feel about each of these **skills**? Colour ✎ in the bars.

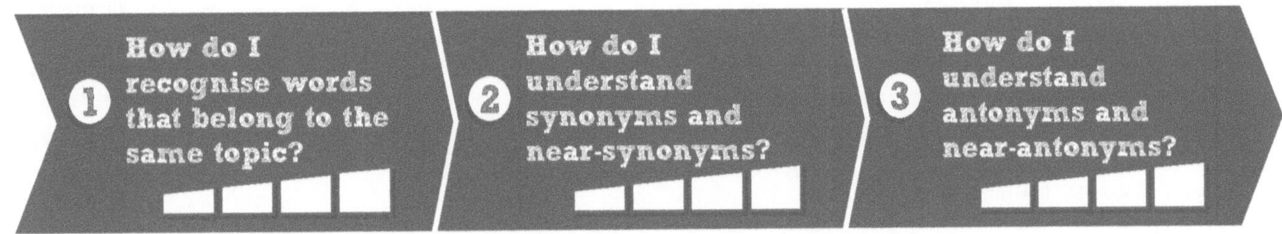

1 How do I recognise words that belong to the same topic?
2 How do I understand synonyms and near-synonyms?
3 How do I understand antonyms and near-antonyms?

This unit will help you to infer meaning. The skills you will build are to:

- infer ideas such as positive and negative
- infer opinions and justifications
- infer meaning by combining information from different parts of the text.

In the exam, you will be asked to tackle reading exercises like the two on these pages. This unit will prepare you to respond to these types of exam questions.

Do not answer this question yet. You will be asked to come back to it at the end of the unit.

Exam-style question

Part-time jobs

What do young Swiss people think about their part-time jobs? Read these four entries on Twitter.

Write the first letter of the correct name in the box.

Write **L** for **Lara**.

Write **S** for **Sara**.

Write **E** for **Emilia**.

Write **M** for **Melina**.

> @_Schweiz – Ich finde meinen Job im Restaurant nicht nur schwierig und mühsam, sondern auch amüsant. Es kommt darauf an, ob die Kunden froh oder sauer sind.
> **Lara**

> @_Schweiz – Ich mache meinen Job sehr gern, da ich mich für Mode interessiere. Meine Chefin gibt mir einen Rabatt auf die Kleidung. Das genieße ich.
> **Sara**

> @_Schweiz – Mein Job gefällt mir, denn ich kann meine Hausaufgaben machen oder fernsehen. Ich denke, er ist sehr einfach, obwohl er nicht gut bezahlt ist.
> **Emilia**

> @_Schweiz – Ich habe die Nase voll von meinem Job. Ich habe die Kunden und meine Chefin satt! Ich muss einen neuen Job finden, um Geld zu verdienen!
> **Melina**

1 Who doesn't enjoy her job? ☐ **(1 mark)**

2 Who finds her job easy? ☐ **(1 mark)**

3 Who enjoys her job sometimes? ☐ **(1 mark)**

4 Whose job matches her interests? ☐ **(1 mark)**

5 Who wants to find a new job? ☐ **(1 mark)**

Get started

Do not answer this question yet. You will be asked to come back to it at the end of the unit.

Exam-style question

Die Arbeit

Read the contributions by four teenage boys on a web forum page, where young people exchange information about their future plans.

Write the first letter of the correct name in the box.

Write **T** for **Tim**.

Write **G** for **Gabriel**.

Write **D** for **Diego**.

Write **M** for **Mathias**.

> Mein Traumberuf ist Journalist. Ich interessiere mich sehr für die Nachrichten und lese auch gern. Im Moment schreibe ich Artikel für die Schulzeitung und meine Freunde meinen, dass sie prima sind. Das ist bestimmt keine einfache oder sichere Arbeit, aber ich glaube, dass es sich lohnt. **Tim**

> Ich hoffe auf eine Karriere in der Musik. Ich bin Gitarrist in einer Gruppe und wir spielen seit drei Jahren zusammen. Wir haben viele Fans, die unsere Musik hervorragend finden. Für mich ist ein Leben ohne Musik ummöglich, obwohl meine Eltern Angst haben, dass ich nichts verdienen werde. **Gabriel**

> Ich möchte eine gute Stelle mit einem großzügigen Gehalt finden. Ich habe keine Ahnung, was ich machen werde, aber das finde ich nicht wichtig. Ich denke, dass es möglich ist, als Vlogger oder YouTuber Millionen von Euro zu verdienen. **Diego**

> In der Zukunft werde ich als Tänzer arbeiten. Mit sechs Jahren habe ich schon angefangen zu tanzen und ich kann mir nicht vorstellen, in einem Büro oder einem Geschäft zu arbeiten. Das finde ich entsetzlich. Meine Eltern sind dafür, dass ich als Tänzer trainiere. **Mathias**

1 Whose main aim is to earn a lot of money? ☐ **(1 mark)**

2 Whose parents are concerned about his choice of career? ☐ **(1 mark)**

3 Who thinks his future job will be difficult? ☐ **(1 mark)**

4 Who prefers an active job? ☐ **(1 mark)**

5 Who has no idea what he wants to do? ☐ **(1 mark)**

The three key questions in the **skills boosts** will help you infer meaning.

1 **How do I infer ideas such as positive and negative?**

How do I infer opinions and justifications?

How do I infer meaning by combining information from different parts of the text?

How do I infer ideas such as positive and negative?

In order to infer ideas such as positive and negative, you need to scan the text and highlight words which have positive or negative emotions and experiences associated with them.

① Adjectives can convey positive or negative emotions. Complete the table by sorting the adjectives in the box into positive and negative. List any antonyms (opposites) together.

~~schwierig~~	mühsam	amüsant	froh	sauer	hervorragend
entsetzlich	~~einfach~~	mühelos	langweilig	prima	furchtbar

Positive	Negative
einfach	*schwierig*

② Verbal phrases are also often used to convey positive or negative emotions. Draw lines to match the English phrases with their German equivalents.

A I enjoy that	**a** Ich habe die Nase voll von
B I like doing my job	**b** Ich mache meinen Job gern
C I enjoy my job (my job pleases me)	**c** Das genieße ich
D I have had enough of	**d** Ich interessiere mich sehr für
E I am fed up with	**e** Mein Job gefällt mir
F I'm very interested in	**f** Ich habe … satt

③ Look out for the negative constructions which are often associated with negative emotions and experiences. Translate the sentences below into English.

Learn these key negative constructions:
nicht einmal = not even
nicht mehr = no longer
nichts = nothing
noch nicht = not yet, still not
gar nicht / überhaupt nicht = not at all
niemand = no one
nie / niemals = never
nirgendwo / nirgends = nowhere

a Mein Job gefällt mir gar nicht.

I don't like my job at all.

b Ich werde nie einen Job finden!

c Ich arbeite nicht mehr im Geschäft.

d Niemand will als Babysitter arbeiten.

e Ich mache meinen Job überhaupt nicht gern.

f Ich habe noch nicht angefangen.

2 How do I infer opinions and justifications?

Recognising expressions which imply opinions is an extremely important skill. Look for the key phrases used to introduce an opinion or adjective. When looking for justifications in a text, you can also use your knowledge of conjunctions to help you, as a justification is often preceded by a conjunction.

1 Find the key opinion phrases in the text below and write each one next to its English equivalent. Circle each phrase as you find it.

Ich arbeite seit zwei Jahren in einem Sportgeschäft. Ich finde meine Kollegen sehr nett und freundlich und ich denke, dass die Arbeit sehr einfach ist. Man hat gute und schlechte Tage und es kommt darauf an, ob die Kunden froh oder sauer sind. Meine Eltern meinen, ich sollte einen neuen Job finden, weil er schlecht bezahlt ist. Ich glaube, dass es sich lohnt, weil der Job sehr flexibel ist. Es ist bestimmt möglich, einen besseren Job zu finden und ich hoffe, nächsten Sommer mehr Geld zu verdienen.

a I find = *Ich finde*

b I think ....

c It depends on ....

d My parents think ....

e I believe ....

f It's worth it ....

g It's certainly possible ....

h I hope ....

Dass often follows the key opinion phrases above. Looking for and underlining *dass* in a text can therefore help you to find opinions and justifications.
The following phrases are sometimes followed by *dass*, but they are also sometimes followed by a comma without *dass*:
Ich denke, dass
Ich finde, dass
Ich glaube, dass

2 Translate the sentences into English.

Remember that *dass* sends the verb to the end and that the word order is therefore different in English and German.

a Meine Freunde meinen, dass meine Artikel prima sind.
My friends think that my articles are great.

b Ich glaube, dass es sich lohnt.
....

c Meine Eltern haben Angst, dass ich nichts verdienen werde.
....

d Ich denke, dass es möglich ist, als Vlogger oder YouTuber Millionen von Euro zu verdienen.
....
....

e Meine Eltern sind dafür, dass ich als Tänzer trainiere.
....

f Ich denke, es ist sehr einfach.
....

3 How do I infer meaning by combining information from different parts of the text?

In order to infer meaning from different parts of a text, make sure you have read and understood all of it. Look for connections – can you spot linked vocabulary and synonyms? Can you connect parts of the text relating to different time frames by spotting time phrases and tenses? Have you understood the structure of the text?

Linked vocabulary could have the same root or be linked by meaning, e.g. *Post – Brief – Briefträger(in) – schicken.*

1 Read the text below. The circled words are used as headings in the table below. Find vocabulary linked to those headings in the text and write the words in the correct column.

Im Moment studiere ich Japanisch und Chinesisch an einer Universität in Berlin. Ich studiere gern in Berlin, weil es eine interessante Stadt ist, die nicht weit von meiner Heimatstadt entfernt ist.

Ich hoffe, nächstes Jahr in Japan und China zu studieren. Im September werde ich einen Kurs an der Universität von Peking beginnen und sechs Monate später werde ich wahrscheinlich als Deutschassistentin in einer Schule in Japan arbeiten.

Ich interessiere mich sehr für Fremdsprachen und möchte meine Kenntnisse von asiatischen Sprachen verbessern. In der Zukunft hoffe ich, Koreanisch, Thailändisch und Vietnamesisch zu lernen, um Korea, Thailand und Vietnam besser kennenzulernen.

Nach der Universität werde ich nach Thailand auswandern und einen Sommerjob in einem Restaurant finden. Mein Traum ist es, in Asien zu wohnen und dort bei einer internationalen Firma zu arbeiten. Ich will mich dort integrieren, also ist es nötig, diese Fremdsprachen zu lernen.

Japan	China	Universität	Sprachen	arbeiten
			Japanisch,	

2 Look at the text in 1 again.

a Write a heading for each paragraph in English in the table below.

b Underline the time phrases used in each paragraph. The first one has been done.

c Write the tense used in each paragraph (past, present or future) in the table below.

Paragraph	Heading	Tense
1	*My university studies*	*Present*
2		
3		
4		

Your turn!

Here is an exam-style question which requires you to practise the skills you have worked on, in particular how to infer meaning.

Remember to look for positive and negative attitudes and opinions. Which phrases will you look out for?

Exam-style question

Part-time jobs

Which job did these young Austrian people want to do when they were younger? Read their posts on a forum.

Write the first letter of the correct name in the box.

Write **B** for **Bruno**.

Write **M** for **Manfred**.

Write **R** for **Roland**.

Write **W** for **Werner**.

Als Kind wollte ich Arzt werden, aber heute will ich das überhaupt nicht machen, da das Medizinstudium sehr lange dauert und ich Angst vor Blut habe! In der Zukunft möchte ich als Pilot arbeiten. Ich denke, dass dieser Beruf prima ist. **Bruno**

Als ich klein war, interessierte ich mich für Tiere und wollte auf einem Bauernhof wohnen. Jetzt möchte ich das nicht mehr machen. Ich interessiere mich für Musik, denn sie ist hervorragend und amüsant. Ich möchte deswegen Musik studieren. **Manfred**

Mit fünf Jahren wollte ich Feuermann werden und das ist heute noch mein Traum. Obwohl das eine mühsame und schwierige Arbeit ist, glaube ich, dass es sich lohnt. **Roland**

Als ich in der Grundschule war, spielte ich stundenlang Fußball. Es war mein Traum, Fußballprofi zu werden. Jetzt gefällt mir Leichtathletik besser, aber ich werde nie Berufssportler werden. Ich möchte lieber als Manager bei einer internationalen Firma im Ausland arbeiten. **Werner**

1 Who still wants to do the same job as when he was little? ☐ **(1 mark)**

2 Whose former dream job now scares him? ☐ **(1 mark)**

3 Who wanted to be a professional sportsperson? ☐ **(1 mark)**

4 Who wanted to work in the countryside? ☐ **(1 mark)**

5 Who wants to work abroad? ☐ **(1 mark)**

(1) Some of the adjectives in the extracts have been highlighted in pink. Write whether they are positive or negative.

....

(2) Some opinion phrases in the extract have been highlighted in green. Find the corresponding justifications and circle them.

(3) Now complete the exam-style question.

Your turn!

Here is a second exam-style question which requires you to practise the skills you have worked on, in particular how to infer ideas such as positive and negative, spot opinions and justifications, and understand meaning by spotting connections between different parts of the text.

Exam-style question

Work

Read the statements written by four teenage girls who are applying to work in a restaurant.

Write the first letter of the correct name in the box.

Write **E** for **Elsa**.

Write **H** for **Hilde**.

Write **C** for **Claudia**.

Write **A** for **Adele**.

Ich bin sehr zuverlässig und geduldig. Ich suche einen Ferienjob im Restaurant, um Erfahrung zu bekommen. Nächstes Jahr werde ich eine Lehre als Köchin beginnen, denn ich möchte in der Zukunft mein eigenes Restaurant haben. Ich freue mich, neue Leute kennenzulernen und bin sehr freundlich. **Elsa**

Ich suche einen Job im Restaurant, weil das interessant und amüsant ist. Letzten Sommer habe ich als Kellnerin gearbeitet und dieser Job hat mir gut gefallen. Ich bin sehr fleißig und ich konzentriere mich gut. Ich hoffe auf eine Karriere in der Touristik und werde nächstes Jahr Touristik studieren. **Hilde**

Ich habe nie im Restaurant gearbeitet, aber letzten Sommer habe ich in einer Bäckerei gearbeitet. Das hat viel Spaß gemacht. Meine Sprachkenntnisse sind sehr gut und ich spreche fließend Englisch und Italienisch. Ich suche einen Job, weil ich Geld für meine Studien brauche. **Claudia**

Ich freue mich auf einen Ferienjob im Restaurant, da ich gern arbeite, obwohl das manchmal mühsam und schwierig ist. Ich mache gern eine aktive Arbeit, weil das nie langweilig und oft lustig ist. Letzten Sommer hatte ich einen Job als Touristenführerin und das war prima. **Adele**

1	Who has previously worked in a restaurant?	☐	(1 mark)
2	Who speaks more than one language?	☐	(1 mark)
3	Who wants a career in catering?	☐	(1 mark)
4	Who describes herself as outgoing?	☐	(1 mark)
5	Who prefers an active job?	☐	(1 mark)

Review your skills

Check up

Review your response to the exam-style questions on pages 55 and 56. Tick ✓ the column to show how well you think you have done each of the following.

	Not quite ✓	Nearly there ✓	Got it! ✓
inferred ideas such as positive and negative	☐	☐	☐
inferred opinions and justifications	☐	☐	☐
inferred meaning by combining information from different parts of the text	☐	☐	☐

Need more practice?

Go back to pages 50 and 51 and do the exam-style questions there. Use the checklist below to help you.

Checklist Before I give my answers, have I ...	✓
identified words indicating positive and negative emotions and experiences?	
recognised expressions which imply opinions?	
recognised reasons or justifications for opinions (with or without connectives)?	
spotted connections in different parts of the text, enabling me to infer meaning?	

Top tips to help you use conjunctions to infer meaning:

Justifications are sometimes introduced by conjunctions. Make sure you know these key conjunctions:

*da** = as / because

denn = as / since

nicht nur ... sondern auch ... = not only ... but also ...

*ob** = whether

*obwohl** = although

um ... zu = (in order) to

*weil** = because

*These conjunctions send the verb to the end.

How confident do you feel about each of these **skills**? Colour in the bars.

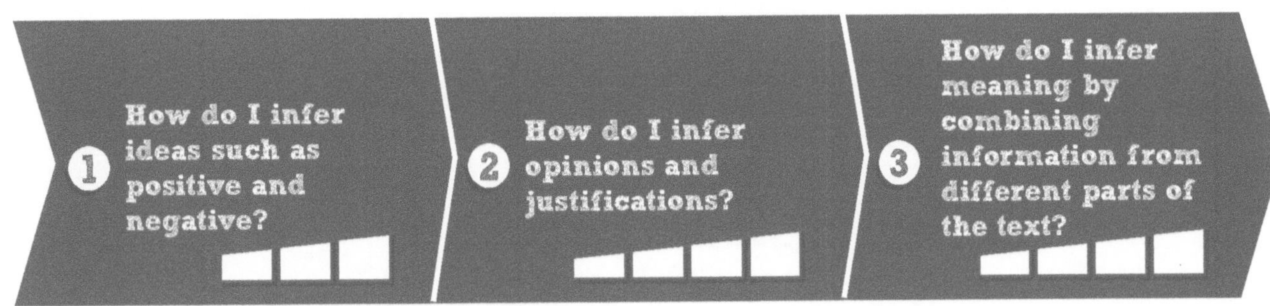

1 How do I infer ideas such as positive and negative?
2 How do I infer opinions and justifications?
3 How do I infer meaning by combining information from different parts of the text?

Translating accurately into English

This unit will help you to translate accurately. The skills you will build are to:

- include all key elements of the original text with no extra or irrelevant material
- use knowledge of word order to accurately sequence ideas
- avoid distorting the meaning of whole sentences.

In the exam, you will be asked to translate a German text of about 35–40 words into English.

This unit will prepare you to look out for potential difficulties and make sure you produce the best possible translation into English.

Do not answer this question yet. You will be asked to come back to it at the end of the unit.

Exam-style question

You and your family are going to a German music festival.

Translate this information about the festival into **English** for your family.

Das ist ein berühmtes deutsches Musikfestival. Normalerweise hört man Bands und Sänger aus europäischen Ländern und den Vereinigten Staaten. Das Festival beginnt am Freitag und endet am Sonntag. Wir werden mit dem Auto fahren und können auf dem Campingplatz zelten.

(9 marks)

How will I translate *Das ist?*

Thinking about word order, how will I translate the start of sentence 2?

Which country is mentioned here?

What tense should I use for the last sentence?

Get started

Do not answer this question yet. You will be asked to come back to it at the end of the unit.

Exam-style question

Your family is going to a football match in Germany.

Translate this information about the game into **English** for your parents.

Das Spiel findet in München statt. Wir werden mit dem Flugzeug von London nach München fliegen und dann mit dem Bus ins Stadion fahren. Wenn wir wollen, können wir in einem Hotel übernachten. Es gibt im Stadion ein kleines Restaurant.

(9 marks)

....

....

....

....

....

....

? How will I translate the key phrase *findet … statt*?

....

? What is the English name of the town *München*?

....

? How will I translate *Wenn*?

....

? How will I translate *Es gibt*?

....

The three key questions in the **skills boosts** will help you translate accurately.

How do I include all key elements with no extra or irrelevant material?

How do I use my knowledge of word order to accurately sequence ideas?

How do I avoid distorting the meaning of whole sentences?

Skills boost

1 How do I include all key elements with no extra or irrelevant material?

It is important to check that you have accounted for every word of the German text in your English translation. Sometimes you will need to add in an extra word so that the sentence makes sense in English, but also check you have not included any extra information that is not present in the German text.

1. Complete the English translations with the correct article, negative or connective.

a Eine Freundin nimmt oft Drogen.	.... friend often takes drugs.
b Mein Freund raucht, weil ihm das Spaß macht.	.... friend smokes, ... he thinks it is fun.
c Er trinkt nie auf Partys.	He .... drinks at parties.
d Ich finde, dass Drogen schrecklich sind.	I think .... drugs are terrible.
e Sie schläft manchmal auf der Straße.	She sometimes sleeps on .... street.

2. Complete each translation with the correct verb in the correct tense. The first one has been done.

a Letztes Jahr haben wir eine Solaranlage installiert.	Last year we *installed* a solar panel.
b In der Zukunft werden wir Energie sparen.	In the future we .... energy.
c Als ich klein war, wollte ich Elektriker werden.	When I was little I .... to become an electrician.

Sometimes an article isn't used in German but would be used in English, so you need to add one in. In this context, *Elektriker* (= electrician) doesn't have an article.

d In den Sommerferien werde ich Deutsch in einer Schule in Bali unterrichten.	In the summer holidays, I .... German in a school in Bali.
e Gestern Abend sind wir auf ein Musikfest gegangen.	Yesterday evening we .... to a music festival.

3. When translating into English, sometimes you will need to add an extra word that is not needed in German. Sometimes you will need to miss out a word that is present in the German. Look at the translations below. Underline the extra word(s) in the English or in the German.

Example:

Ich möchte später Lehrerin werden.	I want to become <u>a</u> teacher later.
a Man kann effektiver recyceln.	We can recycle more effectively.
b Man kann am schnellsten den Müll trennen.	We can separate rubbish most quickly.
c Das größte Problem in der Schweiz ist die Abholzung.	The biggest problem in Switzerland is deforestation.
d Für mich ist die Arbeit sehr wichtig.	For me work is very important.
e Er ist Arzt und arbeitet im Krankenhaus.	He is a doctor and works in the hospital.

Check you have correctly translated comparative (more ...) and superlative (most ...) adjectives.

2 How do I use my knowledge of word order to accurately sequence ideas?

German word order has many specific rules. For example, the verb is always the second idea of a main clause. This means that if there is a time phrase at the start of the sentence, the verb and subject will change places.

When separable verbs separate, the verb is the second idea of the sentence and the separable preposition goes to the end of the sentence.

1 Read each sentence in English, then write the words in brackets into the correct places in the German.

a Normally we hear bands and singers. (*man / hört*)

Normalerweise .... Bands und Sänger.

b The game takes place in Munich on Saturday. (*findet / statt*)

Am Samstag .... das Spiel in München ....

c Next month we will go by car. (*wir / werden / fahren*)

Nächsten Monat .... mit dem Auto ....

d I went to a music festival last year. (*ich / bin / gegangen*)

Letztes Jahr .... auf ein Musikfest ....

e If we want, we can stay in a youth hostel. (*wir / wollen / übernachten / wir / können*)

Wenn ...., ...

in einer Jugendherberge ....

Some conjunctions send the verb to the end of the sentence. These conjunctions include *da, dass, ob, obwohl* and *weil*. When you see one of these words, you will need to look for the verb at the end of the sentence.

2 Underline the verbs in the main clause and the subordinate clause and then complete the translations in English.

a Ich rauche nicht, weil ich das nicht mag.

I don't .... because I don't .... it.

b Ein Problem ist, dass viele junge Leute Alkohol trinken.

A problem .... that many young people .... alcohol.

c Wenn wir wollen, können wir an der Universität studieren.

If we ...., we .... at university.

d Obwohl das sehr teuer ist, fliegen wir nach München.

Although it .... very expensive, we .... to Munich.

German sentences use adverbs and adverbial phrases in a strict order. You always write them in the order: Time, Manner, Place. In English, it's more usual to place the time phrase at the end of the sentence.

3 In each German sentence below, highlight the time, the manner and the place phrases in different colours. Then translate the sentences, changing the order of the phrases as necessary so your English sentences sound natural.

a Wir können am Samstag mit dem Auto ins Stadion fahren.

We can go to the stadium by car on Saturday.

b Die Olympischen Spiele finden 2028 in Los Angeles statt.

....

c Lara wird heute Abend auf der Straße schlafen.

....

3 How do I avoid distorting the meaning of whole sentences?

Look carefully at the rubric and introduction to the task, as well as the text itself. You are aiming to write a translation which stays close to the German but sounds natural in English.

Look out for cognates, 'false friends', synonyms, antonyms and idioms.

1 Underline the cognate, near-cognate or 'false friend' in each of the German sentences below. Then complete the translations.

- a Das ist ein berühmtes deutsches Musikfestival. — It's a famous German *music festival*.
- b Im Gymnasium mache ich keinen Sport. — In ...., I don't do sport.
- c Das Festival beginnt am Freitag und endet am Sonntag. — The .... on Friday and .... on Sunday.
- d Wir können in einem Hotel übernachten. — We can stay in a ....
- e Sie sind sehr arm. — They are very ....

2 Draw lines to match the German sentences with the English translations using your understanding of synonyms and antonyms.

Thinking of a synonym or an antonym in English can be very helpful if you are trying to translate a sentence but don't know the exact meaning of the word given. It can help you to stay relatively close to the text and therefore avoid distorting the meaning.

A Viele Jugendliche sind obdachlos.	a In this area, water pollution is a major problem.
B Arbeitslosigkeit ist ein großes Problem.	b If it doesn't rain, then people go hungry.
C In dieser Region ist Wasserverschmutzung eine große Gefahr.	c Many young people don't have a roof over their head.
D Dürre kann Hungersnot verursachen.	d Not having a job is a big problem.

3 The key idioms below have been incorrectly translated. Write the correct translation above each crossed-out translation.

Idiomatic phrases are tricky to translate in any language, so it is important to learn those on the core vocabulary list so you recognise them in the examination.

- a Das kommt darauf an, ob die Preise gut sind. — ~~It comes on that on~~, whether the prices are good.
- b Ich habe die Nase voll von meiner Schwester. — ~~I have the nose full of~~ my sister.
- c Es ist mir egal, ob wir ins Kino oder ins Restaurant gehen. — ~~It's equal to me~~ if we go to the cinema or to the restaurant.
- d Im Großen und Ganzen wohnen wir gern in der Großstadt. — ~~In the big and whole~~ we like living in the city.
- e Meine Mutter geht mir auf die Nerven, weil sie sehr streng ist. — My mother ~~goes me on the nerves~~ because she is very strict.

Your turn!

Here is an exam-style question which requires you to practise the skills you have worked on, in particular how to translate accurately into English.

Remember to focus on negatives, connectives, time phrases, verbs in different tenses and comparative and superlative adjectives and adverbs.

Exam-style question

Your German penfriend spent her holiday at a nature camp.

Translate her message into **English** for your family.

Ich bin gestern von meinen Abenteuerferien in den Bergen zurückgekommen. Die Landschaft war schöner als zu Hause. Wir sind durch die Wälder gegangen und haben im Freien übernachtet. Ich habe viele wilde Tiere gesehen, aber nie einen Hasen.

(9 marks)

....

....

....

....

....

....

....

....

....

....

1. How many of the following can you spot in the text above? Write the number in the box.
   - a negatives ☐
   - b connectives ☐
   - c time phrases ☐
   - d verbs in the past tense ☐
   - e comparative adjectives ☐
2. Now translate the text in the exam-style question.

Your turn!

Here is a second exam-style question which requires you to practise the skills you have worked on, in particular how to translate accurately into English. Use the checklist below to help you.

Exam-style question

You and your family want to recycle while on holiday in Germany.

Translate this information about recycling into **English** for your family.

> Leere Flaschen und Gläser kommen in den roten Altglascontainer. Zeitungen, Zeitschriften, Kataloge, Broschüren, Papier und Bücher muss man in den blauen Altpapiercontainer werfen. Man sollte Obst und Gemüse im braunen Biocontainer kompostieren. Metall gehört in den grünen Container und Plastik in den gelben Container.

(9 marks)

....

....

....

....

....

....

....

....

....

....

Checklist **Before I give my answers, have I ...**	✓
accurately translated articles, negatives and connectives?	
accurately translated different verb tenses and time phrases?	
accurately translated comparative and superlative adjectives and adverbs?	
added in or left out words where appropriate?	
used my knowledge of German and English word order?	
identified cognates, 'false friends', synonyms, antonyms and idioms?	

Review your skills

Check up

Review your response to the exam-style questions on pages 63 and 64. Tick ✓ the column to show how well you think you have done each of the following.

	Not quite ✓	Nearly there ✓	Got it! ✓
included all key elements with no extra or irrelevant material	☐	☐	☐
used my knowledge of word order to accurately sequence ideas	☐	☐	☐
avoided distorting the meaning of whole sentences	☐	☐	☐

Need more practice?

Go back to pages 58 and 59 and do ✎ the exam-style questions there.

Top tips to help your translation flow naturally:

1. Always check the accuracy of your English. Read your translated text back to yourself.
2. Check you have used English spellings and punctuation and you have got the verb tenses right.
3. Ask yourself the following:
   - Does it sound like an English sentence? (Check the word order if not.)
   - Do any conjunctions send the verb to the end of the clause?
   - Have I avoided incorrect translations of 'false friends'?

How confident do you feel about each of these **skills**? Colour ✎ in the bars.

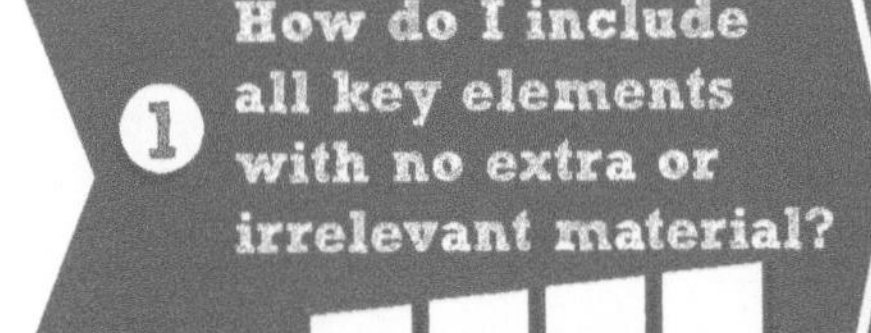

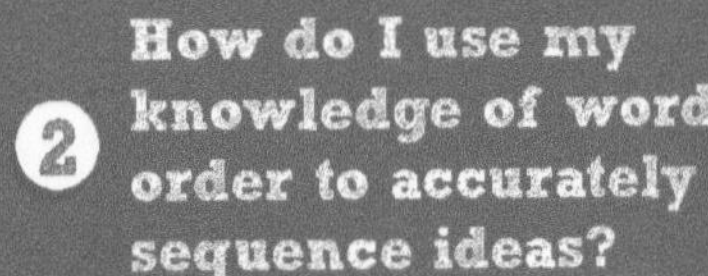

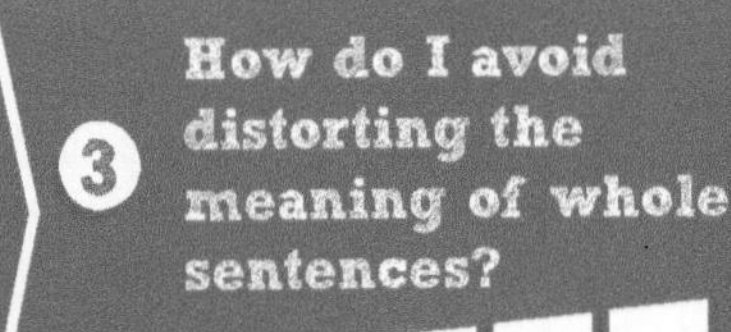

9 Understanding unfamiliar language

This unit will help you to use a range of clues to understand language you have not encountered before. The skills you will build are to use clues from the context, from the surrounding material, and from the unfamiliar words themselves.

This unit will prepare you to respond to Higher reading exercises like the two on these pages. Do not answer this question yet. You will be asked to come back to it at the end of the unit.

Exam-style question

School

You are on a train to Hamburg and read this article about integration at school.

Answer the questions in **English**.

> Ich habe mich auf meinen ersten Schultag in Deutschland gefreut. Im Flüchtlingsheim, wo ich wohnte, gab es keine richtige Schule. Als ich noch in Syrien wohnte, bestand keine Möglichkeit, in den Unterricht zu gehen, weil das zu gefährlich war.
>
> Ich wollte wieder zur Schule gehen, aber ich wusste, dass meine Sprachkenntnisse nicht sehr gut waren. Während der Sommerferien habe ich Deutsch gelernt und viel Deutsch gesprochen, um mit meinen Schulkameraden besser zu kommunizieren.
>
> Die ersten Wochen waren sehr schwierig, weil ich nichts richtig verstand und sehr viele Hausaufgaben machen musste. Ich fühlte mich oft sehr unglücklich und hilflos. Zum Glück hat sich die Lage langsam verbessert und ich fühle mich jetzt viel entspannter. **Zada**

1 How did Zada feel about starting school in Germany?

....

(1 mark)

2 Why wasn't she able to go to school in her home country?

....

(1 mark)

3 How did she prepare during the summer holidays?

....

(1 mark)

4 What did she have to do during the first few weeks?

....

(1 mark)

5 How does she feel about school now?

Write the correct letter in the box.

A	B	C
unhappy	lucky	relaxed

☐

(1 mark)

Get started

Do not answer this question yet. You will be asked to come back to it at the end of the unit.

Exam-style question

Social media

You are on a flight to Munich and read this article on how the media affects the body image of young Germans.

Answer the questions in **English**.

> Schon mit vier Jahren haben Kinder eine Idee von dem „perfekten" Körper. Helden und Prinzessinnen aus Kinderfilmen sind oft hübsche Männer und schöne, schlanke Frauen.
>
> Soziale Netzwerke haben einen starken Einfluss auf das Körperbild von Jugendlichen. Verfälschte Bilder zeigen unrealistische Idealkörper.
>
> Was kann man dagegen machen?
>
> - In der Schule muss man lernen, dass gesund sein wichtiger als perfekt sein ist. Man sollte auch lernen, dass Bilder oft verändert oder verfälscht sind.
> - Zu Hause sollte man gesunde Vorbilder finden, die durch ihre Arbeit und Einstellung inspirieren können, wie zum Beispiel berühmte Athleten oder Schwimmer.
> - Alle Kinder sollten die Gelegenheit haben, Sport zu machen.

1 When do children begin to develop the concept of the 'perfect' body?

....

(1 mark)

2 What has a strong influence during adolescence?

....

(1 mark)

3 How can schools help to fight unrealistic body images?

....

(1 mark)

4 What kinds of role models should be encouraged at home?

....

(1 mark)

5 What should children be able to do?

Write the correct letter in the box.

A	B	C
Play competitive sport	Eat healthily	Do sport

☐

(1 mark)

The three key questions in the skills boosts will help you use different clues to understand unfamiliar language.

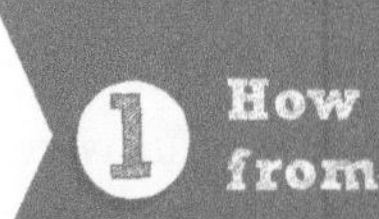

How do I use clues from the context?

How do I use clues from the surrounding material?

How do I use clues from the unfamiliar words themselves?

How do I use clues from the context?

In order to use clues from the context, look carefully at the heading and introduction to the task. Use these to find out the topic and to help you predict the likely content of the text.

Your general knowledge and your knowledge of German-speaking countries can also help you to predict the meaning of words.

1 Look at the headings and introductions below and predict what you think each reading text is likely to be about. Highlight the key words in the introduction and then write your predictions.

A general understanding of current issues in Germany will give you clues as to why integration might be an important issue for schools before you look at the article.

a **Exam-style question**

School

You are on a train to Hamburg and read this article about integration at school.

It could be about ...

b **Exam-style question**

Social media

You are on a flight to Munich and read this article on how the media affects the body image of young Germans.

2 You won't have time to do this in the exam, but it can be useful to make a list of any key vocabulary you think you might see. You could take key words from the heading and introduction as a starting point. Add any extra words you think are relevant to the first column in the table and then complete the second column.

School = *Schule*	Social Media = *Soziale Medien/Netzwerke*
Starting school = *Schulanfang* First day of school = *erster Schultag* Refugee = *Flüchtling* Asylum seeker = *Asylbewerber* Racism = *Rassismus*	

3 Now look at the text excerpt below and highlight any vocabulary you have already predicted in the first column of the table above.

School

Ich habe mich auf meinen ersten Schultag in Deutschland gefreut. Im Flüchtlingsheim, wo ich wohnte, gab es keine richtige Schule. Als ich noch in Syrien wohnte, bestand keine Möglichkeit, in den Unterricht zu gehen, weil das zu gefährlich war.

Ich wollte wieder zur Schule gehen, aber ich wusste, dass meine Sprachkenntnisse nicht sehr gut waren. Während der Sommerferien habe ich Deutsch gelernt und viel Deutsch gesprochen, um mit meinen Schulkameraden besser zu kommunizieren.

2 How do I use clues from the surrounding material?

You don't need to understand every word to understand the main points of a text. You can often make guesses about the possible meanings of unfamiliar words using the words around the unfamiliar word.

Ask yourself whether you can simply ignore a word or whether it is essential for understanding the text. If it isn't essential, then you only need to have a general understanding of what the word might be referring to or might mean. Using grammatical clues is helpful here. Could the word be a noun, a verb or an adjective?

1 In each of the sentences below, an unfamiliar word has been highlighted in yellow. Clues to the meaning of this word have been highlighted in green. Can you infer the possible meaning of the unfamiliar word? Write a brief answer and a possible translation in English.

a Meine kleine Schwester ist immer lebhaft und oft störend.

Adjective, could mean annoying / irritating / lovely / cute

b Es bestand keine Möglichkeit, zur Schule zu gehen.

....

c Erneuerbare Energien wie Solarenergie sind manchmal effektiver als traditionelle Energien.

....

d Soziale Netzwerke haben einen starken Einfluss auf das Körperbild von Jugendlichen.

....

e Ich bin großer Fan von traditionellen schweizerischen Sportarten wie Steinstoßen.

....

f Ich esse gern Obst und Gemüse, am liebsten Spargel. Das finde ich lecker.

....

Try the same technique with any particularly tricky sentences. Is it essential to understand this sentence to answer the questions or is it a sentence you can ignore for now? If it is essential, look at the sentences around the tricky sentence for clues.

2 Read through the short paragraphs below. A student has underlined a sentence they are finding difficult in each paragraph. Circle the key words or phrases in the sentences immediately before and after which you think give clues to the meaning of the difficult sentence.

a Ich wollte wieder zur Schule gehen, aber ich wusste, dass meine Sprachkenntnisse nicht sehr gut waren. Während der Sommerferien habe ich Deutsch gelernt und viel Deutsch gesprochen, um mit meinen Schulkameraden besser zu kommunizieren.

b Ich fühlte mich oft sehr unglücklich und hilflos. Zum Glück hat sich die Lage langsam verbessert und ich fühle mich jetzt viel entspannter.

c Schon mit vier Jahren haben Kinder eine Idee von dem „perfekten" Körper. Helden und Prinzessinnen aus Kinderfilmen sind oft hübsche Männer und schöne, schlanke Frauen.

d Zu Hause sollte man gesunde Vorbilder finden, die durch ihre Arbeit und Einstellung inspirieren können, wie zum Beispiel berühmte Athleten oder Schwimmer.

3 How do I use clues from the unfamiliar words themselves?

Looking at the components of unfamiliar words can help to work out their meanings. Ask yourself:

- How does the word start?
- How does the word end?
- Is it a compound noun where I know the meaning of one or more of the key parts?
- Is it a verb which has an adjective in the middle?

Prefixes in German are often also prepositions and knowing the preposition can help to unlock the meaning of the unfamiliar word. For example, *aussteigen* uses *aus* which often means 'out'.

1 Circle the common prefix in each of these words and write it on the line, along with its translation. Then work out the meaning of the whole word and note it down too.

a (ab)fahren – *ab = from; abfahren = to go from or to leave*

b aufgeben ……

c durchfallen ……

d mitmachen ……

e ankommen ……

f zumachen ……

Nouns in German often end with a suffix. Knowing the common suffixes and spotting other core vocabulary can help you to piece together the meaning of a word.
-chen is a diminutive and often means 'little'
-er is often used for masculine jobs and nationalities and translates as '-er' or '-or'
-in is often used as an ending to feminine forms of jobs and nationalities
-heit and *-keit* are often used for abstract concepts and sometimes translate as '-ity'
-schaft often translates as '-ship' in English.

2 Underline the common suffix in each of these words. Then write the core component of each word on the line, along with their translations. Finally, work out the meaning of the whole word and note it down too.

a der Lehr<u>er</u> *lehren = to teach; Lehrer = teacher*

b die Briefträgerin ……

c das Kätzchen ……

d die Gleichheit ……

e die Persönlichkeit ……

f die Partnerschaft ……

3 Understanding the component parts of compound nouns is very helpful in deciphering the meaning of the word. The two parts of each word below are highlighted. Use them to help you translate the whole word into English.

a der Schultag ……

b das Körperbild ……

c der Schulkamerad ……

d das Flüchtlingsheim ……

e die Sprachkenntnisse ……

f der Idealkörper ……

Your turn!

Here is an exam-style question which requires you to practise the skills you have worked on, in particular how to use clues from the context, the surrounding material or from the unfamiliar words themselves.

Exam-style question

Leisure

You are on a train to Zurich and read this article about eSports.

Answer the questions in **English**.

Letzten Monat hat die SwitzerLAN in Bern stattgefunden. SwitzerLAN ist ein Festival für E-Sports und letztes Jahr haben 1000 Spieler an virtuellen Wettkämpfen teilgenommen. E-Sports sind nicht nur für Computerfreaks, sondern auch für alle, die gern Sport oder Videospiele machen.

Während E-Sports in der Schweiz ziemlich unbekannt sind, sind sie in vielen anderen Ländern sehr beliebt, besonders in Asien (in Südkorea, Japan und China zum Beispiel). Es gibt in diesen Ländern mehrere Ligen für E-Sports und der schweizerische E-Sports-Verband möchte hier in der Schweiz auch Ligen organisieren und finanzieren.

Viele Sportclubs, Sportvereine und Mannschaften wie der FC United Zürich wollen E-Sport-Teams gründen und Verbindungen zwischen E-Sportlern und Sportlern herstellen. Um E-Sports zu machen, muss man trainieren und fit sein, weil sie sehr anstrengend sind. E-Sports sind gesund!

1 What did participants in SwitzerLAN do last year?

....

(1 mark)

2 Who is encouraged to do eSports?

....

(1 mark)

3 Where are eSports well-established?

....

(1 mark)

4 What does the Swiss eSports organisation want to do?

....

(1 mark)

5 Why do you need to train to play eSports?
Write the correct letter in the box.

A	B	C
They're complicated.	It's an elite competition.	They're tiring.

☐

(1 mark)

① Before reading the text, look at the heading and the introduction and predict what the content is likely to be about and what vocabulary you think you are likely to see. Then highlight the vocabulary in the text.

② Now complete the exam-style question.

Your turn!

Here is a second exam-style question which requires you to practise the skills you have worked on, in particular how to use clues from the context, the surrounding material or from the unfamiliar words themselves.

Exam-style question

Houses

You are on a plane to Innsbruck and read Sara's blog post about an environmentally friendly house. Answer the questions in **English**.

> Meine Familie und ich wohnen in einem energiesparenden Haus. Wir haben eine Solaranlage auf dem Dach installiert und versuchen, Energie und Wasser zu sparen.
>
> Das Haus ist aus Holz und Glas und ich finde es sehr schön. Das Erdgeschoss ist sehr hell, mit einem riesigen Wohnzimmer, einem Esszimmer, einer tollen Küche und vielen Fenstern und Glastüren. Im ersten Stock gibt es vier Schlafzimmer und jedes Schlafzimmer hat ein eigenes Badezimmer. Im Dachboden haben wir ein Arbeitszimmer für meine Eltern und ein Spielzimmer für meine Geschwister und mich. Draußen gibt es eine große Terrasse, wo wir essen und uns entspannen können.
>
> Um das Haus haben wir einen großen Garten mit vielen Bäumen und Blumen. Im Garten haben wir auch Nistkästen für Vögel gebaut und mein Vater hat auch einige Bienenvölker. Der Honig ist sehr lecker. Auf der Wiese hinter dem Haus lebt eine kleine Herde Alpakas. Sie sind sehr lustig, aber nicht immer sehr freundlich!

1 In what ways do Sara and her family try to help the environment?

....

(1 mark)

2 What does Sara think of her house?

....

(1 mark)

3 What do they do on the terrace?

....

(1 mark)

4 What have they done to encourage nature?

....

(1 mark)

5 What does Sara think of the alpacas?

Write the correct letter in the box.

A	B	C
funny	friendly	fast

☐

(1 mark)

Review your skills

Check up

Review your response to the exam-style questions on pages 71 and 72. Tick the column to show how well you think you have done each of the following.

	Not quite	Nearly there	Got it!
used clues from the context			
used clues from the surrounding material			
used clues from the unfamiliar words themselves			

Need more practice?

Go back to pages 66 and 67 and do the exam-style questions there. Use the checklist below to help you.

Top tips to help you translate unfamiliar near-cognates:

When you encounter unfamiliar near-cognates, you can sometimes substitute a letter or letters to find the English word:

Durst (change *D* to th) → thurst → thirst

Pfeffer (change *Pf* to p) → peffer → pepper

halb (change *b* to v or f) → half

Now try these: *Wasser* (change *ss* to t), *Recht* (change *ch* to gh).

Checklist Before I give my answers, have I ...	✓
used the rubric and introduction to predict content and vocabulary?	
used grammatical clues to infer the meaning of unfamiliar words?	
underlined tricky sentences and used the sentences around them to infer the meaning?	
used my knowledge of prefixes, suffixes and compound nouns to understand unfamiliar words?	

How confident do you feel about each of these **skills**? Colour in the bars.

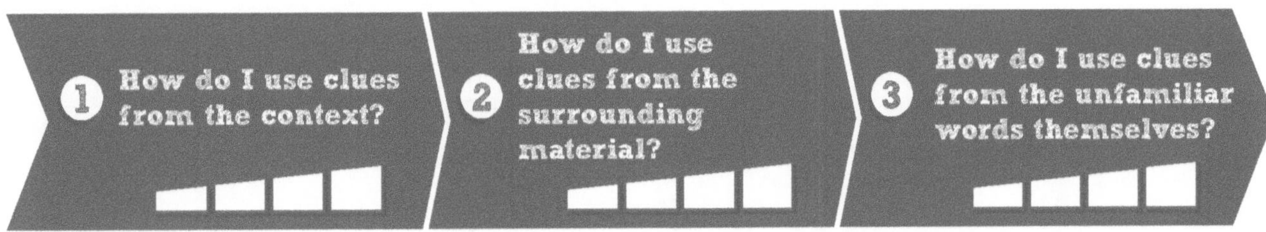
1 How do I use clues from the context?
2 How do I use clues from the surrounding material?
3 How do I use clues from the unfamiliar words themselves?

Answers

Unit 1

Pages 2–3

1 grades pressure
2 bad marks
3 resit the year
4 hard/difficult
5 school trip
6 easy
7 lots of things/new trainers
8 he broke his leg
9 getting up at six/early

Page 4

Type of word	Colour	Examples from text
Adjectives	green	schwierig, schlecht, streng, erfolgreich
Connectives	pink	weil, denn, wenn, sondern auch
Intensifiers	orange	sehr, viel, ziemlich
Nouns	yellow	Gymnasium, Notendruck, Angst, Noten, Eltern, Zeugnis
Verbs	blue	ist, gibt, habe, sind, bin, werde, sitzen bleiben, müssen, bekommen

2

Ich freue mich auf die Schule, weil ich dieses Jahr sehr interessante neue Fächer lerne. Es ist auch total prima, dass ich meine Freunde jeden Tag sehe. Das macht viel Spaß. Ich habe Angst vor den Klassenarbeiten, weil ich sie sehr stressig finde, aber meine Lehrerinnen und Lehrer sind meistens sehr nett und geduldig.

Type of word	Examples from text	English translations
Adjectives	*interessant* *neu* *prima* *stressig* *nett* *geduldig*	interesting new great stressful nice patient
Connectives	*weil* *dass* *aber* *und*	because that but and
Intensifiers	*sehr* *total* *viel* *meistens*	very totally a lot mostly
Nouns	*Schule* *Jahr* *Fächer* *Freunde* *Tag* *Spaß* *Angst* *Klassenarbeiten* *Lehrerinnen und Lehrer*	school year subjects friends day fun fear tests teachers
Verbs	*ich freue mich auf* *lerne* *ist* *sehe* *macht* *habe* *finde* *sind*	I look forward to learn is see makes have find are

Page 5

1 (any 10 of the following:)

Type of word	Examples from text	English translations
Adjectives	*neunte* *schwierig* *stressig* *interessante* *historische* *einfach*	ninth difficult/hard stressful interesting historic easy
Connectives	*dass* *denn* *da* *weil*	that because/for because/as because
Intensifiers	*sehr* *total* *besonders*	very totally particularly
Nouns	*Klasse* *Prüfungen* *Jahr* *Klassenfahrt* *Stadt* *Lieblingsfach* *Geschichte*	class exams year school trip town favourite subject history
Verbs	*sagt* *ist* *freue mich auf* *sind* *fahren* *finde*	says is look forward to are go find

2
- a die neunte Klasse
- b ich freue mich nicht auf
- c ich freue mich auf
- d Lieblingsfach
- e Geschichte

3 i, ii

Circle and annotate:

mitspielen – to play too / to join in the game
Vorstellung – performance
entspannend – relaxing

iii

a Tina enjoys basketball because her friends play too.

b She is looking forward to the theatre group's next performance.

c On Fridays she dances because she finds it very relaxing.

Page 6

1

a	*In der (Informatikstunde) machen wir Computerspiele.*	computer games
b	*Es gibt viele (Pflichtfächer)*	lots of
c	*Wir haben vier Stunden pro (Tag.)*	four lessons
d	*Ich habe schlechte (Noten) und muss sitzen bleiben.*	repeat (school year)
e	*In der (Schule) gibt es 80 Lehrer und 700 Kinder.*	children
f	*Die (Klassenzimmer) sind sehr schmutzig.*	dirty
g	*Ich lerne gern (Mathe), denn ich kann alles verstehen.*	understand
h	*Im (Gymnasium) gibt es 350 Schüler.*	pupils, students

2 a Grammatical clues:

Adjectives = *neu, alt, kaputt, sportlich*

Nouns = *Sachen, Schuljahr, Trainingsschuhe, Sport, AGs, Jahr, Bein, Uhr*

Past tense = *habe gekauft, waren* (third person plural), *habe gebrochen, habe gespielt*

Present tense = *bin, mache, freue mich, muss aufstehen, will aufwachen*

b Lexical clues:

normalerweise, Letztes Jahr, um sechs Uhr, früh

Pages 7–8

1 big and modern
2 very nice but sometimes strict
3 they will learn something practical
4 different countries
5 French or Spanish and Music or Art
6 learnt Arabic
7 is very lovely/recently renovated
8 the new subject PGW (politics–sociology–economics)
9 he likes learning languages

Unit 2

Page 10

1 F
2 R
3 NT
4 R
5 NT
6 R
7 R
8 F

Page 11

1 J
2 S
3 J
4 K
5 J
6 S

Page 12

1 In meiner Freizeit treibe ich gern Sport. Mein Lieblingssport ist **Tennis**. Ich mache auch gern Wassersportarten wie **Rafting**. Zu Hause lese ich gern auf meinem **Tablet**. Meine Lieblingsbücher sind **Thriller**. Ich gehe gern ins Kino und meistens sehe ich **Horrorfilme**. Ich bin auch Musikfan und höre besonders gern **Reggae**.

2

English word	German word	What are the similarities/ differences?	Gender of German cognate
athlete	*Athlet*	Same but without 'e' at the end	Masculine
drama	*Drama*	Same spelling	Neuter
fan	*Fan*	Same spelling	Masculine
fantasy	*Fantasy*	Same spelling	Feminine
film	*Film*	Same spelling	Masculine
find	*finde*	No 'e' in English – German verb ending for *ich*	N/A – verb
fit	*fit*	Same spelling	N/A – adjective
hobby	*Hobby*	Same spelling	Neuter
horror	*Horror*	Same spelling	N/A – adjective
pizza	*Pizza*	Same spelling	Feminine
sport	*Sport*	Same spelling	Masculine
tablet	*Tablet*	Same spelling	Neuter

Page 13

1 a, b

A *amüsant* = amusing, *amerikanische* = American

B *Bananen* = bananas, *bevor* = before

E *Energie* = energy

F *Familie* = family

H *Honig* = honey, *Haus* = house, *historisch* = historical, *hier* = here

I *interessiert* = interested

J *Joghurt* = yoghurt, *japanisch* = Japanese

K *Kajak* = kayak, *Komödien* = comedies, *kreativ* = creative

L *lernen* = learn

O *oft* = often

S *schwimmen* = swimming, *Sommer* = summer, *Schule* = school, *Serien* = series

W *Wasser* = water, *windsurfen* = windsurfing

② a interesting = *interessant*

b English = *englisch*

c Chinese = *chinesisch*

d Spanish = *spanisch*

e musical = *musikalisch*

f allergic = *allergisch*

g fantastic = *fantastisch*

h amusing = *amüsant*

Page 14

①

	German sentence	'False friend'	English word it looks like	What it means in this context	How you worked it out
a	*Am Gymnasium lerne ich Deutsch und Mathe.*	*Gymnasium*	gym(nasium)	grammar school	From the context – you study there.
b	*Der See ist in der Mitte von Deutschland.*	*See*	sea	lake	From the context – it can't be a sea if it's in the middle of the country.
c	*Das ist mein neues Handy.*	*Handy*	handy	mobile phone	Logic – it's a new object.
d	*Ich will einen neuen Computer kaufen.*	*will*	will	want	Grammar – it's a verb, but there isn't another verb, so it can't be future tense.
e	*Ich werde bald windsurfen gehen.*	*bald*	bald	soon	It's a time phrase and it links to the future.
f	*Wir sind fast da.*	*fast*	fast	almost	It's an adverb. *Da* means 'there', so 'almost' is most logical.
g	*Ich segle gern im Boot.*	*Boot*	boot	boat	I know *segeln* means 'sailing', so it must be a boat.
h	*Der Chef ist sehr nett.*	*Chef*	chef	boss	You'd be more likely to say your boss is nice rather than the chef.

② a Underline: Geschenke; Meanings: *Gift* = poison, *Geschenke* = presents

b Underline: lustig; Meanings: *lustig* = funny, *komisch* = strange

c Underline: werde; Meanings: *bekomme* = to receive, *werden* = to become

d Underline: mutig; Meanings: *mutig* = brave, *brav* = well-behaved

e Underline: Rock; Meanings: *Rock* = skirt, *Boot* = boat

f Underline: Gurken; Meanings: *Pickel* = spots, *Gurken* = pickles/cucumbers

Page 15

1 R
2 F
3 NT
4 R
5 NT
6 R
7 F
8 R

Page 16

1 S
2 J
3 K
4 B
5 S
6 K

Unit 3

Page 18

	Past	Present	Future
Axel	swimming	tennis	skiing
Toni	cinema	restaurant	English course
Benno	hockey	table tennis	badminton

Page 19

1 Go to the park
2 Use her mobile phone often
3 After-school activities
4 Use the computer
5 Go out alone
6 Watch television

Page 20

① a yellow

b green

c blue

d *spannend, schlechte, streng* = adjectives; *heute* = time phrase; *ziemlich* = qualifier

e The usual order is subject, verb, direct object.

f The verb always comes second, so the subject comes after the verb.

g After a modal verb, the second verb goes to the end of the sentence before the full stop.

2 a Ich spiele Basketball.

b Sie sieht fern.

c Wir essen Pizza.

d Im Moment trinken wir Orangensaft.

e Wir dürfen ausgehen.

f Ich spiele gern Golf, weil das spannend ist.

3 a Sie gibt (mir) kein Taschengeld.

b Ich kann (ihr) nichts sagen.

c Ich zeige (meinen Freunden) unser neues Haus.

d Ich will (dir) eine Geschichte erzählen.

Page 21

1 a *war, spielte*; imperfect tense

b *gingen*; imperfect tense

c *darf … treiben, habe*; present tense

d *verstehe, spielen*; present tense

e *werde … spielen*; future tense

f *spielt, freut, verbringen*; present tense

2 a was, had

b have

c was, was allowed

d was, was allowed

e could/was able to

Page 22

1 a Ich gehe mit ihnen aus.

b Sie hat immer Zeit für uns.

c Sie gibt es mir.

d Ich darf ihn benutzen, wenn er fertig ist.

e Ich finde sie sehr teuer.

f Wir geben ihn ihr.

g Sie verkaufen ihn dir.

2 a me, her

b her, me

c me, him

d me, them

e her

3 a she; subject pronoun, referring back to sister

b her; direct object pronoun, referring back to mother

c they; subject pronoun, referring back to parents

d them; direct object pronoun, referring back to winter sports

e you; subject pronoun

Page 23

1 Meine beste Freundin heißt Lotte. Sie hat lange, blonde Haare und braune Augen und sie ist sehr schlank. Unser Lieblingshobby ist Leichtathletik – wir sind sehr gute Athletinnen und müssen dreimal pro Woche trainieren. Lotte und ich sind beste Freundinnen, denn ich kann mit ihr über alles reden. Letztes Wochenende sind wir zusammen ins Kino gegangen und wir haben dort eine Komödie gesehen. In den Sommerferien fahren wir nach Spanien. Ich freue mich darauf! **Sabine**

2 Als ich klein war [P], spielte [P] ich oft mit meiner Freundin im Garten. Wir sind [Pr] immer noch Freunde, obwohl ich in Berlin wohne [Pr] und sie in Köln wohnt [Pr]. Wir sehen [Pr] uns nicht oft, aber wir skypen einmal pro Woche. Am Wochenende werde ich nach Köln fahren [F] und wir werden zusammen ins Konzert gehen [F]. Wir sind große Fans von Tokio Hotel. **Thomas**

3 Ich [S] kenne meine Freundin seit drei Jahren. Sie [S] heißt Jenny und ich habe sie [D] in England kennengelernt, weil sie [S] meine Austauschpartnerin war. Letzten Sommer habe ich eine Woche bei ihr [I] in London verbracht und das hat viel Spaß gemacht. Dieses Jahr wird Jenny eine Woche bei mir [I] zu Hause verbringen. Ich [S] werde viel Sport mit Jenny treiben. **Kim**

4

	Past	Present	Future
Sabine	cinema to see a comedy	athletics	going to Spain on holiday
Thomas	garden play with friend	don't see each other often/Skype each other once a week	Thomas will go to Cologne. / They will go to a concert together.
Kim	met friend in England/ spent a week with her last summer	friend is called Jenny	The friend will come to stay/ will spend a week with her. / They will do a lot of sport together.

Page 24

1 Organise a big party
2 Marry in a church
3 Marry abroad
4 Employ a photographer
5 Hire a wedding car
6 Choose a big wedding cake

Unit 4

Page 26

1 Bücher standen unter den Tischen.

2 Es gab Bücher in der Küche und auf dem Klo.

3 Meggie liest beim Frühstück.

4 Manchmal stolperte man über die Bücher.

Page 27

1 Susi wohnt in einem großen Haus/Einfamilienhaus auf dem Land.

2 Die Mutter von Susi arbeitet oft im Garten.

3 Luisa schlief im Zimmer von Susi/hat das Zimmer von Susi geteilt.

4 Sie mussten ruhig bleiben, weil der Vater von Susi arbeitete/arbeiten musste.

Page 28

① Tick: b

② Ad, Ba, Ce, Db, Ec

③ a A

b B

c D

d E

Page 29

① a stood/were in …

b In their house … under the tables, on chairs and in the …

c … because the school starts very …

d a living room/lounge with … and a big kitchen

e … a bathroom and a …

f … a room with her.

② In the ? there is ? a ? and a work-room. Her Dad works at home because he's a(n) ? .

This sentence is about rooms in the house and her dad's job.

Page 30

① Ag, Bd, Cf, De, Ec, Fa, Gb

② a What stood under the tables?

b In which room were there books?

c Who reads at breakfast?

d What sometimes happens with the books/to the books?

③ Ac, Ba, Cb

④ a Woher

b Worauf

c Womit

d Wohin

Page 31

① A mother looks for her son and discovers he has gone.

② Sample answer:

Sie begann ihn zu suchen. Sie trat ins Schlafzimmer. Sie ging in die Küche. Sie sah sogar in der Toilette nach. Sie machte im Korridor Licht und schaute hinter die Schränke. ‚Anton!' rief sie. ‚Komm, mein Junge, ich bin wieder gut! Anton!'

Sie rief bald laut und bald leise und zärtlich. Er war nicht in der Wohnung. Er war fortgelaufen! Sie wurde sehr unruhig. Sie rief bittend seinen Namen. Er war fort.

Er war fort! Da riss sie die Wohnungstür auf und rannte die Treppe hinunter, ihren Jungen suchen.

a She begins to look for him in the apartment.

b She calls him.

c She realises he is gone.

d She goes to look for him outside.

③ a 1, b –, c 2, 3, d 4

④ 1 Sie begann ihn/Anton zu suchen.

2 Sie fühlte sich unruhig.

3 Anton war fort.

4 Sie rannte die Treppe hinunter.

Page 32

① 1 Er wohnte in einem Wohnblock in Berlin.

2 Er wohnt seit fünf Jahren im Einfamilienhaus/dort.

3 Er muss sehr früh aufstehen, um ohne Verspätung in die Schule zu kommen.

4 Er möchte in einem Wolkenkratzer wohnen.

Unit 5

Page 34

1 Sie waren im Restaurant neben dem Hotel.

2 Sie fand es gut, weil sie im Internet surfen konnte.

3 Der Vater von Anna telefonierte.

4 Sie spielte mit ihrem iPod Touch.

Page 35

1 The boys had to go to the museum.

2 He felt sick.

3 Oskar lost his money.

Page 36

① a I; *Axel war* / + time phrase + *in Berlin* / *Er war ...*

b I; *Anna fand* / + *es gut* + *weil* + reason / *Sie fand …*

c P; *Das Essen ist* / + adjective / *Es ist …*

d I; *Das Haar war* / + preposition + noun / *Es war …*

e I; *Axel und seine Freunde waren* / + time phrase + *in Berlin* / *Sie waren …*

f P; *Anna ist* / + adjective / *Sie ist …*

2 a name + *wohnte im Haus.*

b names + *wohnen im Hotel.*

c *Anna* + verb, imperfect.

d number + *Personen sind im Hotel.*

Page 37

1 a Where were Anna and her parents?

b Why did Anna find the restaurant good?

c Who was telephoning?

d What was Anna doing under the table?

2 a *im Restaurant neben dem Hotel* – in the restaurant next to the hotel

b *weil es in Reichweite vom WLAN-Anschluss des Hotels lag und ich … im Internet surfen konnte* – because it was in reach of the hotel Wi-Fi and I could surf the internet

c *Papa … zum Telefonieren hinausging* – Dad … went out to telephone

d *spielst dabei unterm Tisch mit deinem Handy* – you're playing under the table with your phone

Page 38

1 a (Wann) fährt er nach Berlin?

Er fährt am Samstag mit dem Zug nach Berlin.

b (Warum) fährt er nach Berlin?

Er fährt am Samstag nach Berlin, um seine Freunde zu besuchen.

c (Was) hat sie gekauft?

Sie hat ein T-Shirt im Kleidungsgeschäft gekauft.

d (Welchen) Rock trägt sie heute Abend?

Sie trägt den schwarzen Rock, denn er ist sehr hübsch.

e (Wer) fährt mit ihr?

Ihr Bruder fährt mit ihr, weil er sehr lustig ist.

f (Wie) war die Reise?

Die Reise war sehr lang und er hat ein Buch gelesen.

g (Wo) liegt die Jugendherberge?

Die Jugendherberge liegt in der Altstadt und ist sehr groß und modern.

2 a In the morning, they had to go to the museum.

b He felt very sick.

c Oskar lost his money.

Page 39

1 Highlight:

1 *ist, die Stadt*

2 gibt, es

3 kann (sitzen), man

4 kann (machen), man

2 Highlight:

1 *Wie*

2 Was

3 Wo

4 Was

3 Highlight:

1 *hübsch und klein*

2 die Kirche, die alte Burg, die alten Gassen

3 auf einem Feld

4 an den Baggersee fahren

4 1 Die Stadt von Miriam ist hübsch und klein.

2 Es gibt die Kirche und die alte Burg und die alten Gassen.

3 Man kann auf einem Feld sitzen.

4 Man kann an den Baggersee fahren.

Page 40

1, 2

Hallo!

Meine Mutter hatte am Wochenende Geburtstag und wir mussten für sie ein Geschenk kaufen. Meine Schwester und ich sind zusammen einkaufen gegangen.

Zuerst sind wir zum Warenhaus gegangen, aber meine Schwester hat nichts gefunden. Das Kleid war „zu altmodisch", die Bluse war „zu eng" und der Rock war „zu groß".

Zum Schluss (drei Stunden später) sind wir ins Schreibwarengeschäft gegangen. Wir haben dort für unsere Mutter einen bunten Kuli, ein Fotoalbum, eine Duftkerze und ein schönes Notizbuch gekauft. Das nächste Mal werde ich ohne meine Schwester einkaufen gehen. Sie ist sehr nervig!

3 1 They needed to get a birthday present for their mother.

2 a pen / a photo-album / a candle / a notebook

3 She doesn't want to go shopping with her again because she's very annoying.

Unit 6

Page 42

1 F

2 NT

3 T

4 T

5 F

6 T

7 T

8 F

Page 43

C, D, G, H, I, K

Page 44

①

Types of holiday	Weather	Accommodation	Transport
Aktivurlaub	Sonne	Zelt	Zug
Strandurlaub	hageln	Campingplatz	Flughafen
Abenteuerurlaub	regnen	Hotel	
	frieren	Jugendherberge	
	nass	Doppelzimmer	
	kalt	Reservierung	

②

Places in town	Times/Time lengths	Beach	Transport
Flughafen	Stunde	Meer	Flugzeug
Restaurant	Jahr	Sonne	Boot
Schwimmbad	Abend	Strand	Auto
Jugendherberge	Monat	Eis essen	Straßenbahn
Hotel	Tag	Sonnenbaden	Fähre

Page 45

① Ab, Bf, Cd, Da, Ee, Fc

②

	Synonym	Near-synonym
a Urlaub	Ferien	Feiertage
b wolkig	bewölkt	neblig
c Problem	Schwierigkeit	Fehler
d Reservierung	Buchung	Bestellung
e erschöpft	müde	nicht geschlafen
f teuer	kostspielig	hat viel Geld gekostet

③ a schrecklich
- b nass
- c kalt
- d Meer
- e in den Bergen wandern
- f das war unmöglich

Page 46

① Ag, Bd, Ca, Db, Ec, Fh, Gf, He

② a Ich mache nicht gern Aktivurlaub.
- b Ich bin nicht sportlich.
- c Das hat mir nicht gefallen.
- d Wir konnten nicht schlafen.
- e Wir konnten in der Jugendherberge nicht essen.

③ a Circle: schlechte, dreckig, kalt, unglücklich, klein, gefährlich, unsicher [used as adverb here], unfreundlich
- b gute, sauber, warm, glücklich, groß, ungefährlich, sicher, freundlich

Page 47

① Ich wohne in Bern. Das ist die Hauptstadt von der Schweiz. Bern ist eine kleine, historische Stadt. Die Altstadt ist sehr schön. Es gibt auch sechs Brücken, die die Altstadt mit der modernen Stadt verbinden. Bern hat auch mehrere Figurenbrunnen, die in der Mitte des 16. Jahrhunderts gebaut wurden.

Ein Nachteil ist, dass die Einkaufsmöglichkeiten sehr schlecht sind. Ich fahre oft irgendwo anders hin, um einkaufen zu gehen. Am Abend ist es nicht sehr lebendig und man kann nicht einfach ausgehen. Ein Vorteil ist, dass es im Sommer sehr warm ist und man in den vielen Freibädern gut schwimmen kann. Man kann auch in der Aare schwimmen. Das ist ein Fluss, der durch Bern fließt. Er ist sehr kalt und fließt sehr schnell, aber das finde ich prima! **Mia**

1 Bern ist nicht sehr groß.
2 Bern hat neue und alte Stadtviertel.
3 In Bern kann man Museen besuchen. (no pairs)
4 Bern hat viele tolle Geschäfte.
5 Die Stadt hat ein gutes Nachtleben.
6 Im Sommer ist es oft heiß.
7 Mia schwimmt nie.
8 Die Aare ist sehr warm.

② 1 R
2 R
3 NT
4 F
5 F
6 R
7 F
8 F

Page 48

D, F, G, I, J, L

Unit 7

Page 50

1 M
2 E
3 L
4 S
5 M

Page 51

1 D
2 G
3 T
4 M
5 D

Page 52

①

Positive	Negative
einfach	schwierig
mühelos	mühsam
froh	sauer
hervorragend	entsetzlich
	furchtbar
prima	langweilig
amüsant	

② Ac, Bb, Ce, Df, Ea, Fd

③
- a I don't like my job at all.
- b I will never find a job.
- c I don't work in the shop any more.
- d No-one wants to work as a babysitter.
- e I really don't like doing my job.
- f I haven't started yet.

Page 53

①
- a Ich finde
- b Ich denke
- c Es kommt darauf an
- d Meine Eltern meinen
- e Ich glaube
- f Es lohnt sich
- g Es ist bestimmt möglich
- h Ich hoffe

②
- a My friends think that my articles are great.
- b I think that it's worth it.
- c My parents are worried that I won't earn anything.
- d I think that it's possible to earn millions of Euros as a vlogger or YouTuber.
- e My parents are in favour of me training as a dancer.
- f I think it's very easy.

Page 54

Japan	China	Universität	Sprachen	arbeiten
Japanisch	Chinesisch Peking	studieren Kurs	Japanisch Chinesisch Fremdsprachen Koreanisch Thailändisch Vietnamesisch	Deutschassistentin Sommerjob Firma

② a and c

Paragraph	Heading	Tense
1	My university studies	Present
2	Plans for next year/gap year/year abroad	Future
3	Other languages I want to learn	Present
4	What I'm going to do after university	Future and present

b Underline:

Im Moment

nächstes Jahr, Im September, sechs Monate später

In der Zukunft

Nach der Universität

Page 55

① Positive

② Circle:

..., dass dieser Beruf prima ist.

..., denn sie ist hervorragend und amüsant.

..., dass es sich lohnt.

③
1 R
2 B
3 W
4 M
5 W

Page 56

1 H
2 C
3 E
4 E
5 A

Unit 8

Page 58

This is a famous German music festival. Normally you hear bands and singers from European countries and the United States. The festival begins on Friday and ends on Sunday. We will go by car and can camp at the campsite.

Page 59

The game is taking place in Munich. We will fly from London to Munich and then go by bus to the stadium. If we want, we can stay overnight in a hotel. There's a small restaurant in the stadium.

Page 60

1
- a A friend often takes drugs.
- b **My** friend smokes **because** he thinks it is fun.
- c He **never** drinks at parties.
- d I think **that** drugs are terrible.
- e She sometimes sleeps on **the** street.

2
- a Last year we **installed** a solar panel.
- b In the future, we **will save** energy.
- c When I was little I **wanted** to become an electrician.
- d In the summer holidays, I **will teach** German in a school in Bali.
- e Yesterday evening we **went** to a music festival.

3
- a We can recycle more effectively.
- b We can separate the rubbish most quickly.
- c Das größte Problem in der Schweiz ist die Abholzung.
- d Für mich ist die Arbeit sehr wichtig.
- e He is a doctor and works in the hospital.

Page 61

1
- a Normalerweise **hört man** Bands und Sänger.
- b Am Samstag **findet** das Spiel in München **statt**.
- c Nächsten Monat **werden wir** mit dem Auto **fahren**.
- d Letztes Jahr **bin ich** auf ein Musikfest **gegangen**.
- e Wenn **wir wollen**, **können wir** in einer Jugendherberge **übernachten**.

2
- a I don't **smoke** because I don't **like** it.
- b A problem **is** that many young people **drink** alcohol.
- c If we **want**, we **can study** at university.
- d Although it **is** very expensive, we **fly/are flying** to Munich.

3
- a Wir können am Samstag mit dem Auto ins Stadion fahren.

  We can go to the stadium by car on Saturday.
- b Die Olympischen Spiele finden 2028 in Los Angeles statt.

  The Olympic Games will take place in Los Angeles in 2028.
- c Lara wird heute Abend auf der Straße schlafen.

  Lara will sleep on the street this evening.

Page 62

1
- a It's a famous German **music festival**.
- b In **grammar school**, I don't do sport.
- c The **festival begins** on Friday and **ends** on Sunday.
- d We can stay in a **hotel**.
- e They are very **poor**.

2 Ac, Bd, Ca, Db

3
- a **It depends** whether the prices are good.
- b **I am fed up with** my sister.
- c **I don't mind** if we go to the cinema or to the restaurant.
- d **On the whole**, we like living in the city.
- e My mum **gets on my nerves** because she is very strict.

Page 63

1
- a 1 (nie)
- b 2 (und, aber)
- c 1 (gestern)
- d 5 (bin … zurückgekommen, war, sind … gegangen, haben … übernachtet, habe … gesehen)
- e 1 (schöner)

2 Yesterday I came back from my adventure holiday in the mountains. The landscape was more beautiful than at home. We went through the forests and slept in the open. I saw many wild animals but never a hare.

Page 64

1 Empty bottles and glasses go in the red used glass container. You must throw newspapers, magazines, catalogues, brochures, paper and books in the blue used paper container. You should compost fruit and vegetables in the brown bio-container. Metal belongs in the green container and plastic in the yellow container.

Unit 9

Page 66

1 She was looking forward to it.

2 It was too dangerous.

3 She studied and spoke German.

4 Lots of homework.

5 C

Page 67

1 At the age of 4

2 Social networks

3 Schools can help students learn that it is more important to be healthy than perfect/understand that pictures are often changed or falsified

4 Healthy role models such as athletes or swimmers/people who can inspire through their hard work and attitude

5 C

Page 68

1
- a It could be about starting a new school. It might be connected to refugees or asylum seekers. It could be to do with racism in school.
- b It could be about selfies and pictures on social media. It might be connected with people sharing images. It could be about health problems/eating disorders.

Page 69

1 a adjective; could mean annoying/irritating/lovely/cute

b verb – imperfect tense; to exist

c adjective; renewable

d noun; influence

e noun; a sport (stone-throwing)

f noun; a vegetable (asparagus)

2 a Ich wollte wieder zur Schule gehen, aber ich wusste, dass meine Sprachkenntnisse nicht sehr gut waren. Während der Sommerferien habe ich Deutsch gelernt und viel Deutsch gesprochen, um mit meinen Schulkameraden besser zu kommunizieren.

b Ich fühlte mich oft sehr unglücklich und hilflos. Zum Glück hat sich die Lage langsam verbessert und ich fühle mich jetzt viel entspannter.

c Schon mit vier Jahren haben Kinder eine Idee von dem „perfekten" Körper. Helden und Prinzessinnen aus Kinderfilmen sind oft hübsche Männer und schöne, schlanke Frauen.

d Zu Hause sollte man gesunde Vorbilder finden, die durch ihre Arbeit und Einstellung inspirieren können, wie zum Beispiel berühmte Athleten oder Schwimmer.

Page 70

1 a *ab* = from; *abfahren* = to leave

b *auf* = up; *aufgeben* = to give up

c *durch* = through; *durchfallen* = to fall through, to fail

d *mit* = with; *mitmachen* = to do … with …

e *an* = on or at; *ankommen* = to arrive

f *zu* = to; *zumachen* = to close

2 a *der Lehr**er***; *lehren* = to teach; *Lehrer* = teacher

b *die Briefträger**in***; Brief = letter, *tragen* = to carry; *Briefträgerin* = post-woman

c *das Kätz**chen***; *die Katze* = cat; *Kätzchen* = kitten

d *die Gleich**heit***; *gleich* = equal; *Gleichheit* = equality

e *die Persönlich**keit***; *Person* = person; *Persönlichkeit* = personality

f *die Partner**schaft***; *Partner* = partner; *Partnerschaft* = partnership

3 a School day

b Body picture/image

c School friend

d Refugee home

e Knowledge of language(s)

f Ideal body

Page 71

2 1 Took part in virtual competitions

2 Everyone who enjoys sport or video games

3 In Asia (South Korea, Japan, China)

4 Organise and finance leagues

5 C

Page 72

1 They have solar panels on the roof and try to save energy and water.

2 She thinks it's very beautiful.

3 They eat and relax.

4 Built nesting boxes for birds and her father has bee-hives.

5 A

Notes

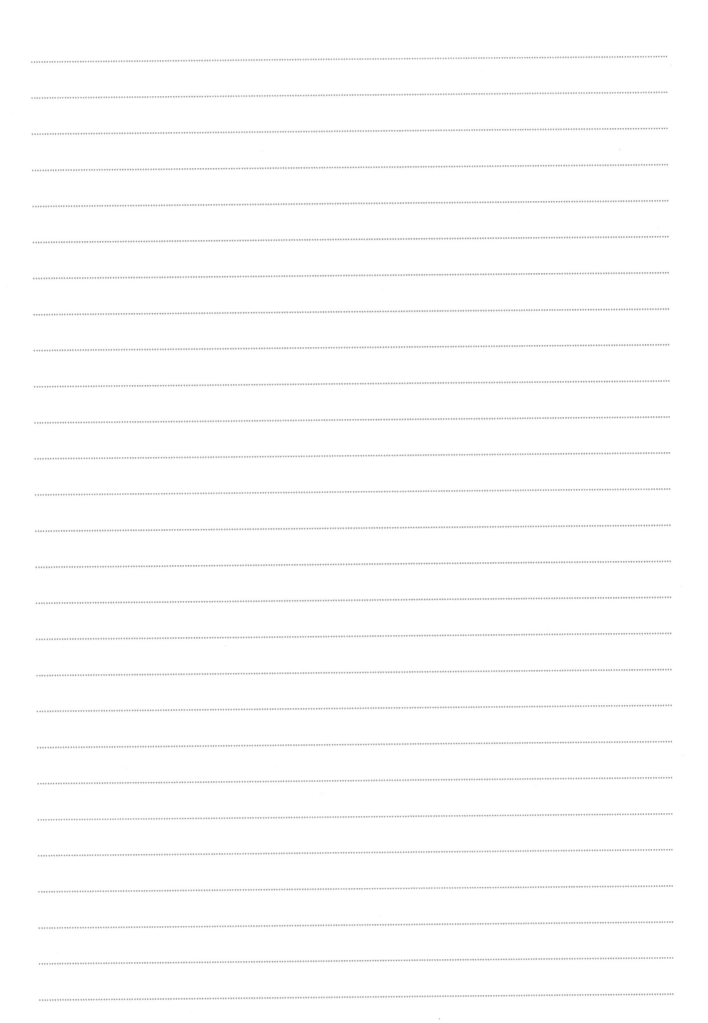